Practical Handbook of Low-Cost Electronic Test Equipment

Robert C. Genn, Jr.

illustrated by E. L. Genn

Parker Publishing Company, Inc.
West Nyack, New York

Library of Congress Cataloging in Publication Data

Genn, Robert C
   Practical handbook of low-cost electronic test equipment.

   Includes index.
   1.   Electronic instruments.   2.   Electronic apparatus
and appliances--Testing.   I.   Title.
TK7878.4.G46   621.3815'48   78-15349
ISBN 0-13-691071-8

The Many Ways This Book

Will Help You Accomplish

More with Low-Cost

Test Equipment

Have you ever wished for a mini-computer programmed to give you fast answers to questions on troubleshooting? Do you hesitate to purchase more expensive test equipment because you're not certain you're getting the most from the equipment you already have? Do you agree that of all the facilities available to the technician-experimenter, test equipment is the most important? Would you like an extraordinarily helpful "assistant" that you can rely on for practical solutions to problems with test equipment? If your answer to these questions is yes, this book has been written for you.

Every chapter is brimming with realistic, simplified techniques that show you how to make inexpensive test equipment do double or triple duty. Packed with special techniques, all based on solid experience, this book will help you get far more out of multimeters, basic oscilloscopes, color TV alignment generators, and a wide range of low-cost test equipment. For example, I don't own an oscilloscope and would like to check the ripple of a DC power supply. No problem. Simply turn to Chapter 1, and you'll find a way to do so with nothing but a volt-ohmmeter (VOM). You'll also discover many new tricks to use with common shop equipment such as transformers, DC power supplies, and soldering guns. Moreover, all of the tests and modifications described in this book will be detailed in the simplest possible way, with procedures that spell out *exactly* what to do, step-by-step.

Chapter 2 will show you how to re-use burned out tubes by using them to construct octal plugs and hook-up cables. In fact, every chapter shows you how to increase the versatility and range of your test gear, providing ideas that will save you time, energy, and money. For example, there is a unique section in this handbook that deals with automotive electrical problems that you can solve quickly and easily with nothing but your VOM.

As another example, did you know that with a few spare parts you can transform a basic, inexpensive scope into one of the most informative, most versatile, and most reliable test instruments you have ever used? The practical know-how is in Chapter 8, and you can probably find the few parts needed in your junk box of odds and ends.

A problem that can be especially tough is measuring decibels of attenuation at a multitude of points on a waveform if you don't have special equipment. Chapter 9 shows you how to make a simple scale that will reduce the time needed to do the job to seconds, and it can be done with any oscilloscope.

All chapters will cover test equipment and troubleshooting procedures that will help you get more out of every piece of test gear in your shop. The last two chapters are comprehensive *practical* guides to modern low-cost TV test equipment and how to use this gear when troubleshooting. Both include detailed guidelines on applications and general test techniques for all the TV test instruments found in the average shop.

It isn't necessary to wade through endless theory or background data to get the *usable* information you need. All you have to do to answer any question is check the index and turn to the page indicated and you'll find realistic advice and simplified techniques for making your test gear do double duty. You will find that we have eliminated all unnecessary, time-consuming material pertaining to electronic theory and have concentrated on subjects that are essential to helping you do your work *skillfully*, *quickly*, and *inexpensively*.

The Bureau of Labor Statistics predicts that close to a half-million electronics engineers and technicians will be employed by industry in the next five to eight years. The number of experimenters and electronics hobbyists will amount to a far greater number. Because of the impressive growth in this field, many authorities are predicting that consumer electronics may become the source of more jobs than any other single industry in the world. Every chapter in this book is full of practical ideas and techniques that are essential for the person who wants to work more successfully with electronic test instruments and equipment in this leading growth industry.

Robert C. Genn, Jr.

Also by the author

Workbench Guide to Electronic Troubleshooting

TABLE OF CONTENTS

Tested Techniques That Make Your Multimeter Do Double Duty

1

This chapter contains tested techniques that will enable you, in effect, to double the value of your multimeter. It will show you how to use your volt-ohmmeter (VOM) as a power monitor, capacitance checker, and induction measuring instrument. It will also enable you to perform a host of other checks and measurements that you may have thought were impossible without purchasing new and expensive equipment.

One area of electronic troubleshooting that many electronic technicians have considerable trouble with is automotive electrical systems. As a bonus, this chapter shows how to use an ordinary VOM to test distributors and ballast resistors, and how to quickly locate blown fuses that you may encounter while working with CB equipment, tape decks, and other electronic gear found in vehicles.

EFFECTIVE VOLTAGE-RIPPLE
CHECKS WITH A VOM

There are many uses for the VOM that most of us do not always apply to our advantage. For example, if I suspect a DC power supply filter system isn't working properly (you'll hear hum in radios or see weaving in TV pictures if there is excessive ripple), I usually grab a scope even when I have a good VOM in my hand—which only proves that it's hard to break bad habits.

If you want to check for excessive ripple voltage with your VOM, all you have to do is set the function switch to AC and measure the power supply's output. When you are making this check, it's better to read the peak-to-peak voltage scale if there is one on your meter. What you'll see on the output depends on the type of filter system you're checking. For example, if you're working on a two-section choke input filter system and the input capacitor opens, you'll see a considerable increase in ripple voltage but very little change in the DC output voltage. But if the output capacitor of the same system opens, you'll see the DC output voltage decrease by a substantial amount and an increase in ripple voltage.

As another example, when you're checking a simple AC-DC power supply like the ones found in many older radio receivers using series string tube filaments—typically, they use half-wave rectifiers and a resistor in place of the filter choke—you'll see a large DC output voltage drop if the input capacitor opens and, of course, a large increase in ripple level. However, if the output capacitor develops an open circuit, you'll see very little change in the output voltage but you will have a large increase in ripple voltage amplitude. As you can see, with just a little experience you can tell a lot about power supply filter circuits from a couple of measurements with your VOM.

To ease the pain of troubleshooting, here are several other possible causes of hum in the output of a power supply.

1. A defective diode in a full-wave rectifier circuit.

2. A defective filter choke.

3. Trouble in the voltage regulator circuit. You'll probably find above-normal load current in this case.

4. Improper soldering (cold soldered joint), broken connections, or incorrect values of component parts can also cause increased ripple. Be sure to check these possibilities.

Sound simple? It is. In fact, these checks are so simple that they are frequently overlooked. Furthermore, they can be real life-savers if you don't have a scope handy. However, if you are working with a regulated supply, it's better to use the procedure given in Chapter 9.

HOW TO USE A VOM AS A
POWER MONITOR

Frequently, a technician needs a wattmeter and one isn't available. Naturally, if a wattmeter is handy it's the best instrument to use. On the other hand, if you don't have one, you can make a simple wattmeter that will determine the power of resistive loads—such as radio and TV receivers—by using a 1 ohm resistor and your voltmeter. To make the measurement, place the 1 ohm resistor in series with the equipment under test and connect your voltmeter as shown in Figure 1-1.

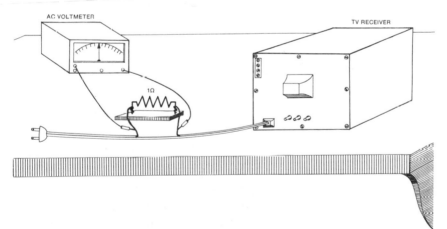

**Figure 1-1: Connections for
measuring power with an
AC voltmeter**

After you have the circuit set up, first measure its line voltage and then measure the voltage drop across the resistor. Now, here's the secret. You'll read 1.0 volt on the meter for each 1.0 ampere of current flowing in the circuit. Therefore, all you have to do is multiply the meter reading by the line voltage reading. For example, if you read 110 volts on the line and 1 volt across the resistor, the power is 110 watts. Incidentally, if you don't have a 1 ohm resistor with the desired wattage rating, you can make one using the heating elements from old electric heaters, electric irons, or discarded toasters.

Let's stop right here and emphasize a few warnings. There are electronics techs who rely on their sixth sense to tell them when they are getting into trouble when working with AC power lines. For the rest of us, there are rules to follow.

1. Remember, ordinary 120 volt household power can kill. *You should not work on energized electrical circuits alone.*

2. When you're servicing power circuits, turn the power off. Place the switch to the off position, pull the plug, or pull a fuse.

3. Never connect any instrument across an AC power line unless you're sure there are no test leads at ground potential. Pay particular attention to VTVMs and TVMs and other meters that have one test lead connected to ground. If you don't, you're sure to see sparks fly and you, plus your equipment, may be ruined!

4. You should use a variable voltage source and increase the power line voltage slowly. This allows you to monitor the current flow and avoid any excessive current.

After you have made the measurement, your next step is to check the manufacturer's plate or instruction manual for the equipment under test. Let's say your power measurement is fairly close to the manufacturer's recommended value. In this case, leave the equipment on for four or five minutes and monitor the voltmeter reading. The reason for doing this is that you want to be sure the piece of heating element doesn't change value when heated.

As soon as you're sure it doesn't change value when heated, you're ready to start making equipment checks. For example, if you're checking a piece of gear and find your reading below the manufacturer's given power rating, the equipment has a partially open circuit. On the other hand, a higher reading indicates a partial short. These are good points to remember because this check is an excellent first step in troubleshooting all types of electronic gear.

TECHNIQUES FOR CHECKING
IN-CIRCUIT CAPACITORS

Another unusual use for your VTVM (or any other high impedance voltmeter) is to find leaking, open, or shorted capacitors rapidly and easily while they are still in the circuit. Furthermore, to check to see if they have changed value, all you need is a clock with a second hand and your voltmeter. When you are making any or all of these checks, your first step is to disconnect the suspected capacitor on the ground side. Now, connect the voltmeter positive test probe to the capacitor lead you have lifted and the negative lead to chassis ground as shown in Figure 1-2.

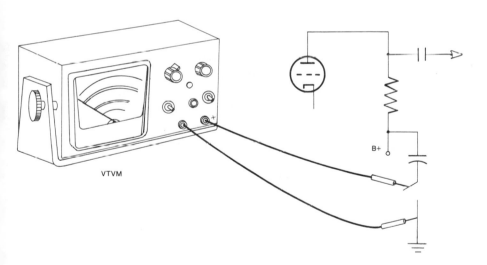

**Figure 1-2: Checking
in-circuit capacitance**

If you suspect the capacitor has changed value, proceed as follows. At the same instant you apply power to the equipment under test, start counting time while watching the sweep second hand on your clock. You'll see the pointer slowly rise to the applied voltage and then drop back to zero. When the pointer reaches zero, stop your time count and record it. Now, you need one more thing—the value of the input resistance of your VTVM. Typically, it will be 11 megohms, and it is usually listed in the operation manual.

Let's assume that it took 55 seconds from the time you applied power until the pointer dropped back to zero. To calculate the approximate value of the capacitor, use the formula:

$$\text{capacitance} = \frac{\text{time}}{(\text{meter resistance}) \times 5}$$

In this case we get:

$$\text{capacitance} = 55 / (11 \times 10^6)\,(5) = 1 \text{ microfarad}$$

This simple test can tell you many things. For example, if your VTVM reads a constant voltage (does not show a rise and fall), this is an indication the capacitor is shorted. But if you don't get any reading, the capacitor is probably open.

As another example, it's possible that the voltage will rise and then drop but won't reach zero. In some cases this means you have a leaky capacitor to replace. However, watch this check! *Electrolytic capacitors* are normally leaky, so the leakage check is not valid for them.

You'll find that you can check all but the small picofarad capacitors with this method. A couple of examples that would prove impossible to measure are: (1) a 1,000 pf capacitor that has a 0.05 second response and (2) a 0.01 μf capacitor that will have only a half-second. There are a few simple rules that can be used to determine when you can see a meter deflection. These are given in Table 1-1.

RESISTANCE	CAPACITANCE	TIME TO REACH THE APPLIED VOLTAGE
R (IN OHMS) × C (IN FARADS) ×5 = T (IN SECONDS)		
R (IN MEGOHMS) × C (IN MICROFARADS) ×5 = T (IN SECONDS)		
R (IN OHMS) × C (IN MICROFARADS) ×5 = T (IN MICROSECONDS)		
R (IN MEGOHMS) × C (IN PICOFARADS) ×5 = T (IN MICROSECONDS)		

**Table 1-1: Rules for determining
when you can see a voltmeter
deflection when checking
capacitance**

HOW TO FIND A TRANSFORMER'S IMPEDANCE RATIO WITH LOW-COST TEST EQUIPMENT

A vital part of all electronic equipment is the transformer. A brand-new stock transformer is very easy to work with because you will normally have all the specs. But have you ever wanted to know the impedance ratio of an unknown power transformer, audio transformer, or flyback transformer? It would be nice if all manufacturers would mark them, but they don't. There is a painless way to find the impedance ratio using nothing but a high impedance voltmeter and an audio oscillator. Connect your equipment as shown in Figure 1-3. After you have everything set up, set your audio oscillator to 60 Hz for a power transformer, 1 kHz for an audio transformer, and about 5 kHz for a TV flyback transformer.

Your next step is to measure the voltage across the primary and secondary. Now all you have to do is divide the larger voltage reading by the smaller one and square the result. This answer is the impedance ratio of the transformer. If you find the larger voltage on the secondary, you have a step-up transformer; if the voltage is

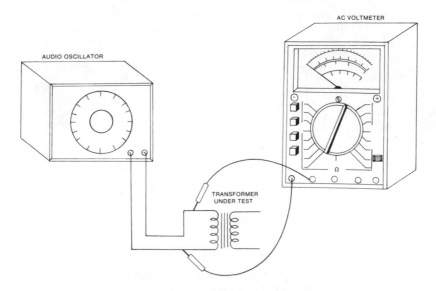

**Figure 1-3: Test set-up for
determining a transformer's
impedance ratio**

greater on the primary, it's a step-down transformer. Incidentally, the turns ratio is the same as the voltage ratio.

Sometimes you can encounter trouble using this method. For example, let's assume you're checking a 120 VAC to 5 VAC step-down power transformer and are using an audio oscillator with a 5 volt output to check it. In this case, you'll have about 0.2 volts on the secondary, which is all but impossible to read. To get out of this dilemma, turn the transformer around and connect your audio oscillator to the secondary. To see what we're doing, all we need to do is realize that 120 VAC is a 24 to 1 step-down transformer. Therefore, turning it around gives us a 24 to 1 step-up transformer. The result with a 5 VAC input is 120 VAC on the output. However, this is too high because we don't want to exceed the windings' voltage insulation rating, so it's better to use 1 volt output from the audio oscillator, which will produce only 24 volts on the winding and is much safer.

A word of caution: Do not connect 120 VAC to the secondary of a step-down transformer and try to make the measurement just described. If you try it, the transformer's insultation might break down due to the high voltage, which could result in damage to the transformer or, even worse, harm to you.

STEP-BY-STEP GUIDE FOR MEASURING INDUCTANCE WITH A VOLTMETER

Don't throw away those unknown chokes and coils. A quick and inexpensive measurement of inductance can be made with your VOM and a potentiometer, and you can use the same system to check one inductor against another. The hook-up is shown in Figure 1-4. The potentiometer should be linear and can be any value. Caution: *Be sure you don't exceed the wattage rating* or you'll have maximum smoke. Also remember, a 1 watt pot means a maximum

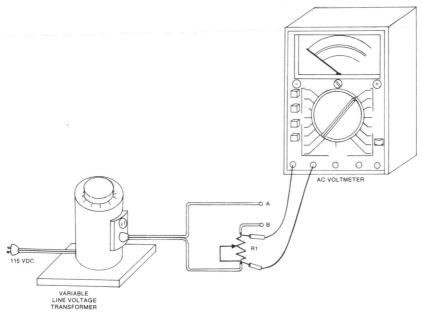

AC VOLTMETER

A

B

R1

115 VDC

VARIABLE
LINE VOLTAGE
TRANSFORMER

Figure 1-4: Hook-up for inductance reading. This wiring diagram is not safe if the variable transformer is an auto transformer. An isolation transformer is recommended during the check.

of 1 watt across 100% of the element, 1/2 watt across 50% of the element, 1/4 watt across 25%, and so on.

There are two ways that you can make the inductance measurement. The first and least expensive way (if you don't own an audio oscillator) is to short the points A and B as shown in Figure 1-4 and adjust the pot (R_1) for full-scale deflection on your voltmeter. The voltage is not critical as long as you don't burn up the pot.

After you have the test circuit set up, calibrate the meter by using inductors with known values. Using this method with a few different potentiometers, you can make a fairly wide range of measurements. However, you can substitute an audio signal generator for the variable line transformer and get a wider range of readings. The following example shows that with a wide range (frequency) audio oscillator and one pot almost any inductor can be checked with this method. Using this procedure to measure an inductor, all you have to do is adjust the pot while measuring voltage across it and the component you have connected to points A and B. When both voltages are equal, *XL equals R*.

Suppose you have an iron core choke and when you measure the resistance value after adjusting the circuit for $XL = R$ you find (using 60 Hz) that the resistance equals 3.8 k ohms. Your next step is to use the formula: $L = XL / (2 \pi F)$. All you need do now is plug the values into the formula and your work should look like this.

$$L = 3800 / 6.28 \times 60 = 3800 / 376.8 = 10 \text{ henrys}$$

You'll find these methods of measuring inductance are simple, fast, accurate, and two more ways to get around buying new test gear by using the equipment you have on hand.

A SUCCESSFUL WAY TO MEASURE
THE IMPEDANCE OF AN INDUCTOR
WITH A VTVM

A very good way to measure the impedance of a power supply filter choke, or any similar inductance, is to place your audio signal generator and a 10 ohm resistor in series with the choke as shown in Figure 1-5. Then set the generator to 60 Hz and measure the voltage across the resistor and inductor. When the voltage measurement

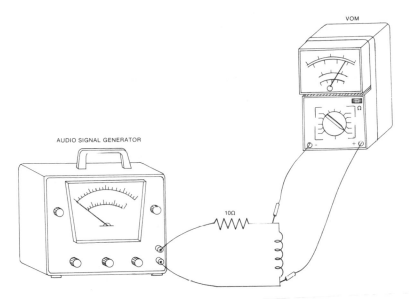

**Figure 1-5: Circuit connections for
measuring an inductor's impedance**

across the resistor is being made, it's possible to short out the
inductor unless either the voltmeter or the audio generator is
floating—in other words, not grounded.

All you have to do now is calculate the impedance by using the
formula:

$$\text{impedance} = \frac{\text{voltage across choke}}{\text{voltage across resistor} \times 0.1} \text{ or,}$$

$$\textbf{Z} = (\textbf{E}_{\text{choke}}) / (\textbf{E}_{\textbf{R}} \times 0.1)$$

Let's assume that you measured 3 volts across the choke and 4 volts
across the resistor. To find the impedance of the choke, you would
do the calculations as follows:

$$\textbf{Z} = \textbf{E}_{\text{choke}} / \textbf{E}_{\textbf{R}} \times 0.1 = 3 / 4 \times 0.1 = 3 / 0.4 = 7.5 \text{ ohms}$$

The accuracy of your measurement will depend on the tolerance of
the 10 ohm resistor. The closer to 10 ohms, the better. You'll find
that this procedure will work very well for checking the impedance

of transformers and many other type inductors, such as relays and so forth.

USING A VOLTMETER TO MEASURE
RESISTANCE IN MEGOHMS

If you pick up a several megohm resistor and try to measure its value with a standard ohmmeter, you'll quickly find out that it's all but impossible to do. Most us us tend to assume that an ohmmeter's highest range is its upper limit. But it's very easy to read right on up to thousands of megohms using the following procedure. The circuit connections are as shown in Figure 1-6. By carefully examining the

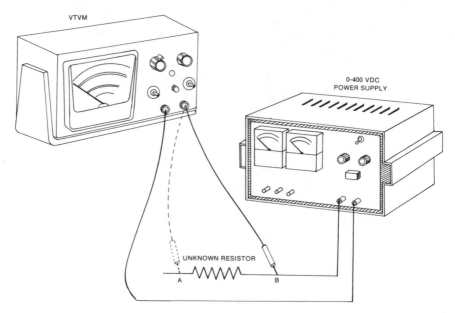

**Figure 1-6: Resistance
measurements in megohms
with a voltmeter**

diagram, you can see that all we're doing is setting up a simple voltage divider using the voltmeter's input impedance as one of the resistances.

First, set your VTVM (or other higher impedance meter) function switch to DC volts. Next, measure and record the voltage at points A and B. Finally, use the following formula to calculate the value of the resistor.

$$\text{resistance in megohms} = \frac{11\ (\text{volts at A}) - (\text{volts at B})}{\text{volts at B}}$$

Here's an example. Say that you set the power supply output at 400 volts; then you measure 385 volts at A and 1.5 volts at B. Placing the voltage readings in the formula, we get:

$$\text{resistance in megohms} = \frac{11\ (385) - (1.5)}{1.5} = \frac{4218.5}{1.5} = 2812.3$$

This method of determining resistance in megohms is fast, and you don't have to buy additional equipment. Try this technique the next time you run into a problem reading those very high resistance values. It just might save the day.

HOW TO USE YOUR SOLDERING GUN AND OHMMETER TO CHECK AUDIO TRANSFORMERS AND SPEAKERS

If you want a quick and easy way to check a speaker and output transformer, reach for your soldering gun and your problem is solved. Simply energize the soldering gun and hold it close to the transformer. If you hear a 60 Hz hum from the speaker, both are okay. If you don't hear a hum, get out your ohmmeter. Some transformers may have sufficient magnetic shielding to prevent the magnetic coupling. However, you can still isolate the problem with the ohmmeter.

To test the speaker, *tap* the test leads of the ohmmeter on the voice coil terminals. No sound? If not, this is an indication that the voice coil could be bad. It's probably out of kilter and rubbing on the side of the speaker magnet or housing. Or, it's possible the coil is open. To check this possibility, watch your ohmmeter. If the ohmmeter shows no reading (when you're tapping the coil terminals), the voice coil is open. But if you do hear clicks, the speaker and voice coil are good and your next logical step is to examine the secondary of the transformer.

HOW TO TEST AN AUTOMOTIVE
DISTRIBUTOR WITH A VOM

There are areas other than electronics where we can put our VOM to work. For example, one of the biggest headaches in the world is caused by a car that is hard to start or won't start. One of the things that causes this problem is too much resistance in the points in the distributor. To see if this is the problem, all you have to do is pick up a voltmeter, because, as we all know, a high resistance causes an increased voltage drop.

When you are making the measurement, you'll have to use the lowest range on your VOM. Some meters have a 0 to 100 millivolt range, but many others have a lowest range of 0 to 0.5 volts. The meters with millivolt ranges are best for the following measurements, but if you have a VOM with a 0 to 0.5 volt range, you can still successfully troubleshoot the distributor.

First, remove the distributor cap and energize the starter for short periods of time until you see that the points are closed. Next, connect the voltmeter to the points listed in Table 1-2. The maximum voltages you should read are listed in the right-hand column. Any voltage readings that are higher than those listed indicate trouble in that circuit. If your voltmeter's lowest range is 0 to 0.5 volts, you should see very little, if any, meter readings when doing the checks.

Voltmeter Connection	Maximum voltage reading
Between the movable arm of the breaker points to the breaker plate	0.2 volts or 200 millivolts
Between the distributor primary terminal of the coil to the movable arm of the breaker points	0.05 volts or 50 millivolts
Between the breaker plate and the distributor metal case	0.05 volts or 50 millivolts
Between the distributor metal case and the engine block	0.05 volts or 50 millivolts

Table 1-2: Distributor, voltage
checks with a VOM

GUIDE TO CHECKING AN AUTOMOTIVE
BALLAST RESISTOR WITH A VOM

If the breaker points in your car's distributor are showing indi-
cations of burning, it's possible that the ballast resistor is allowing
excessive current to flow in the circuit. It's very easy to check this
possibility out with your voltmeter, and you don't have to call in an
automotive mechanic.

To make the test, first set your voltmeter to the 50 to 30 volt
range, depending on what type voltmeter you have, and connect the
positive lead to the positive terminal of the battery. Then connect
the negative lead to the plus terminal of the car's ignition coil. Your
next step is to place a jumper lead from the negative terminal of the
coil to chassis ground. Figure 1-7 shows the necessary connections.

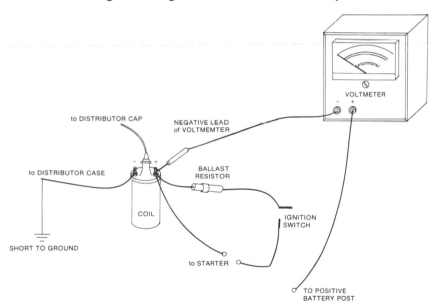

Figure 1-7: Checking an automotive
ballast resistor with a VOM

After you have made all connections, turn the ignition switch
on and read the voltmeter. If you read about 6 volts ± 2 volts, the
ballast resistor is good. However, if you read 2 or 3 volts, the

resistance is too low, and that's why your points are burning.

There is an exception. If you read zero volts, it's possible the resistor is inside the coil. To find out if this is the case, disconnect the coil leads and use an ohmmeter to measure the resistance of the coil. If the resistor is inside the coil, you'll measure about 4 ohms ± 1 ohm. Typically, you'll find that the coils designed to use an external current limiting resistor (usually about 1.5 ohms) will measure between 1 to 2.5 ohms.

KEY STEPS TO CHECKING AN
AUTOMOTIVE IGNITION SWITCH
WITH A VOM

As mentioned before, if you're like me, there's nothing that will frustrate you more than a stubborn car that is hard to start, or even worse, won't start. The current limiting resistor is usually shorted (bypassed) when you energize the starting switch of your car. This is to permit a high current to get to the coil to help during starting. If the resistor isn't bypassed, it can make the car hard to start and that's when the blood pressure starts to rise. The lead connections for this test are the same as shown in Figure 1-7, and the test is usually made at the same time as the current limiting resistor check.

To make the test, set your voltmeter range switch to the 2.5 or 3 volt position. Next energize the starter and watch the voltmeter reading. If the reading is about 1 volt or less (you may have to drop down to a lower range to get a reading), it's good. A higher voltage reading indicates excessive resistance somewhere in the bypass circuit. It could be in the ignition switch or the wires leading to and from the switch. Therefore, you'll have to make point-to-point voltage checks. Incidentally, when you're checking the connections in an automotive wiring system for high resistance, ideally you shouldn't measure more than 200 millivolts across any connection.

IN-CIRCUIT TESTING OF
AUTOMOTIVE FUSES WITH A VOM

If you do any servicing and installing of CB radios, tape decks, and the like in vehicles, sooner or later you probably are going to run into a blown fuse in the automotive electrical system. Often the easiest and fastest way to check a fuse is to substitute it with another known good one. However, you can end up replacing them one at a time, which is a slow, aggravating procedure. The way around this problem is to get out your VOM. It will tell you if the fuse is bad or if it's a wiring problem without even taking the fuse out of the circuit.

Your first step is to set your voltmeter range switch to a position that has a full-scale reading of over 12 volts DC and connect it as shown in Figure 1-8. Next, turn the ignition switch and the equipment which the fuse protects to the on position. The next step is easy. Place the voltmeter leads as shown in Figure 1-8. If you read a voltage, the fuse is blown. If not, the fuse is good. Caution: Read on. There is an exception to this rule! The exception is that it's very possible the fuse is good and the trouble is between the battery and the fuse. To check this, connect the negative lead of the voltmeter to chassis ground. Then take the positive voltmeter lead and

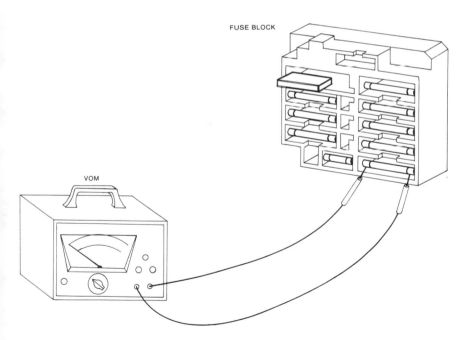

**Figure 1-8: Voltmeter connections
for checking automotive fuses**

touch both sides of the fuse. If you read zero on both sides, start looking for an open in the wiring system.

Another method to check fuses that was suggested to me is to use the VOM's ammeter rather than the voltmeter. The technician who suggested it prefers this method because he can see if:

1. Before he replaces the fuse the current is correct and it was just an old fuse that wore out.

2. If the current is too high, there is a problem at the load end; or if the current is zero when he connects the ammeter across a blown fuse, his next step is to switch to the voltmeter and check the battery terminal.

Getting the Most Out of
Low-Cost Probes and Leads

2

In this chapter you will find many practical suggestions and ideas concerning applications for test probes and test leads. This is not a discussion about theory—it's a *practical guide* full of real-life servicing information on low-cost test probes and leads of all descriptions. This chapter covers them all, giving you the know-how you need to construct and use inexpensive test probes and leads in all types of hook-ups.

With this handy, quick reference guide, you'll increase your ability to make error-free measurements and construct low-cost cable harnesses that you can use every day. It's arranged in easy-to-reference sections that cover using an improved cheater cord, making a DC probe, IF amplifier measurements, high voltage testers, constructing "home brew" octal plugs and tube adapters, and minimizing problems when using a probe with a scope. Selecting a probe can be a very tricky job if you want meaningful broadband measurements. In fact, it's critical to use the right probe and properly match the probe to your scope, or your measurement errors can be as high as 50%.

TIME AND WORK-SAVING
CHEATER CORD

If you think blowing a customer's fuse while servicing a TV receiver is an undesirable side effect, then this section is for you. A simple method to prevent this from happening is to fuse your cheater cord. Figure 2-1 is a pictorial example of how your finished cord should look.

The fuse holder shown in Figure 2-1 was purchased at a local automotive supply house. It is a 20 amp type fuse holder and was placed in one leg of the cheater, as shown. With this simple ounce of prevention, you'll increase your chances of completing more service calls per day and eliminate all those extra difficulties associated with blowing the customer's fuse.

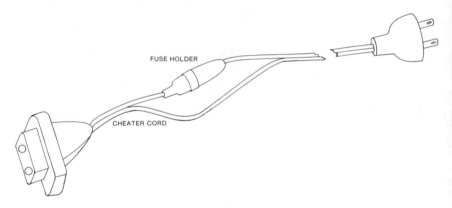

FUSE HOLDER

CHEATER CORD

**Figure 2-1: Circuit connections
for a fused cheater cord**

PRACTICAL TROUBLESHOOTING
TECHNIQUES FOR LOW-COST DC
TEST PROBES

When using many low-cost VTVM's, AC/DC measurements are made with a single probe. For example, the uni-probe used with Eico's VTVM and the one on Heathkit's VTVM both use a single probe. Normally, these test probes have a one megohm resistor mounted in the DC probe. If this resistor develops an open, the plus and minus volts position on the range switch will produce a zero reading when you try to measure a DC voltage. If this happens to you, try using the AC probe to measure a *low* DC voltage.

Let's say you try measuring a known 10 volts DC. If you read about 11 or 12 volts using the AC probe, this is an indication the probe resistor should be repaired or replaced. In case you do have to replace the resistor, it's easy to do. Figure 2-2 shows (with probe cover removed) the resistor placement for the Eico uni-probe.

It's also possible the contacts in the instrument's DC switch sections are loose or broken. To check this section, take an ordinary lead pencil and use the eraser end for tapping and slightly pressing the switch. If there is a loose or broken contact, you'll see the meter operate momentarily during your attempt to measure a DC voltage. By the way, while you have the instrument out of the case, it's a good idea to use a can of aerosol cleaner and spray these components.

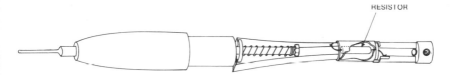

RESISTOR

**Figure 2-2: DC probe resistor
placement**

HOW TO SELECT AND USE THE RIGHT TEST PROBE

If you have lots of money, it's possible to buy electronic test equipment and all the correct probes that will produce readings and displays of signals taken off any point in a TV receiver . . . even the tuner and preamp. However, most of us don't have that kind of money and, furthermore, such large amounts of amplification are not needed. But you should know what type of probe you'll need and when you will, or will not, see a display on ordinary service bench equipment.

For example, if you're working on a radio or TV receiver, you can easily measure the signal of the output of the last IF amplifier, provided you use a demodulator probe with your scope or VTVM. But how about the second IF amplifier input? Maybe—maybe not—and the chances of measuring the signal on the input of the first IF, mixer-oscillator or RF preamplifier, are about a million to one if yours is the type of electronic test gear found around most shops. Incidentally, be careful that you don't touch any high voltage points while you are poking around inside whatever you're testing when using a demodulator probe because they are usually rated for a maximum of 30 volts rms and 500 volts DC and, in some cases, even less.

The other type probe you'll need is a low capacitance scope probe (also called a *high impedance probe*). Frequently you will find these probes have two positions—direct and × 10. The direct position is handy for some measurements, but in almost every case the high impedance probe is more accurate because the direct probe can load down a circuit. You'll need this probe to inspect signals after the receiver's second detector (demodulator).

The simplest impedance probe may be no more than a variable capacitor (usually 6-30 pF) and a resistor (about 10 megohms) connected in parallel. One typical arrangement of electronic components used for a demodulator probe is shown in Figure 2-3.

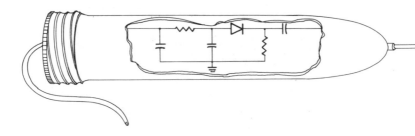

**Figure 2-3: Cut-away view
of inside a typical demodulator
probe**

HOW TO CONSTRUCT A
DEMODULATOR PROBE

You don't have a scope and demodulator probe but need to troubleshoot a receiver's last IF section? No sweat. It's simple to build a circuit that you can use with your VTVM to measure RF voltages. Figure 2-4 shows a circuit that will measure RF voltages right up to about 200 MHz (depending on the type diode you use).

Mount the circuit on a piece of old PC board (keeping your leads as short as possible). Place it in some type of metal container such as a cigar holder, tube shield, or a piece of light weight aluminum tubing that you'll find in almost any hardware store or home-supply center. The shielded cable goes to your VTVM, and the ground side is connected to the metal holder. Use a copper braid grounding lead and alligator clip for the return path from the test circuit, as shown in Figure 2-4.

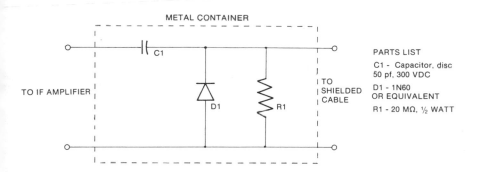

**Figure 2-4: RF probe for
VTVM's**

When you use the circuit, you'll find the readings on your VTVM are peak RF voltage values, if the meter is calibrated to read rms. However, if you want to know the rms values, simply use the formula rms = 0.707 × your peak voltage reading. Another point: When you are making measurements of RF voltages, remember that they should be made with a test signal from a signal generator placed at the receiver antenna terminals or at the input to an IF amplifier, *not* with the receiver tuned to some station.

Finally, of the diodes readily available to most of us, the germanium point contact type is generally the best for RF applications. However, whatever you use, take care that you don't try to measure a very high voltage (30 volts rms in the case of the 1N60). In certain types of diodes (such as the 1N34), the limits are 15 or 20 volts rms. If this presents a problem, you can get around it by connecting two or more diodes in series. Two will double the maximum voltage you can measure, three will triple it, and so on. An excellent place to get the parts you'll need is from a scrapped chassis. Any chassis having a crystal detector will do.

A SURE AND SIMPLE WAY TO MAKE
AN ATTENUATOR PROBE

Most of us tend to assume that if we need an oscilloscope attenuator probe, there's no way around it. We have to purchase one. However, when you realize that it's possible to make a simple one using nothing but a resistor, capacitor and some form of metal holder, it becomes apparent that this is a way to get by until you get the money for a better one. Figure 2-5 shows the two components you'll need.

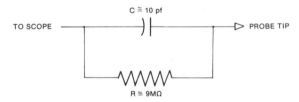

**Figure 2-5: Scope attenuator
probe circuit**

Now, all we need is a probe case. I've found that a good container to use to construct probes is any aluminum cigar holder. To construct the probe metal tip, first drill a hole of the proper size (about 1/8 inch diameter) for a brass screw approximately one inch or longer, in the end of the cigar holder. Next, place a piece of insulating material (spaghetti used to insulate wire is good) on the shank of the brass screw. Now place a fiber washer under the head of the screw and stick the brass screw through the hole in the container. However, it's a good idea to connect a piece of insulated wire (stripped at one end) to the head of the screw and through the container at this point. This is so you'll have something to connect to your electrical circuit.

Your next step is to place another fiber washer on the bolt after it is pushed through the hole in the container. Finally, simply screw on a nut of the proper size, tighten it up, and you are ready to polish up the tip with a grinder. At this point, your holder with tip should look like Figure 2-6.

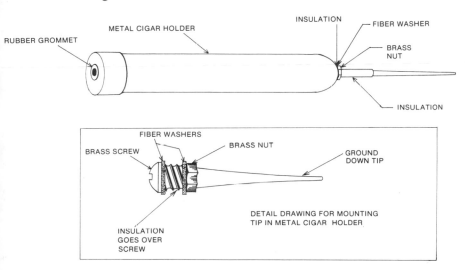

**Figure 2-6: How to construct
an oscilloscope probe**

Some of these cigar holders have a screw-on top. As a general rule, it's easier to use this type. At any rate, drill a hole of the proper size for the probe lead through the cap, then place a rubber grommet in it, and this will finish up your probe case. Now place the 10 pF capacitor and 9 megohm resistor, paralleled, as shown in Figure 2-5, on a piece of old PC board (or any other type mounting board) cut to fit inside the cigar holder. Fit this circuit inside the holder, make the electrical circuit connections, and your probe is completed.

HOW TO MINIMIZE LOW-COST SCOPE/PROBE PROBLEMS

Most of us tend to assume that an oscilloscope display is telling us what is actually happening in a circuit we have under test. This may or may not be true, depending on several factors. For instance, if you select the wrong type of probe, chances are you won't see some of the signal characteristics you're looking for. In fact unless you take certain precautions, especially at high frequencies, getting the signal to your scope can be the toughest job encountered when making a measurement. For example, if you fail to match the probe to the scope, it can result in as much as 50% measurement error. Fortunately, there are three rules that will serve us well under most testing conditions. These are:

1. If you want your loading errors to be less than 1%, select a scope/probe combination with the resistance looking in to the tip of the probe at least 100 times as great as the signal source impedance.

2. To minimize your errors related to frequency, select a scope/probe combination with a shunt capacitance value *as small as possible*.

3. To keep the phase errors at a minimum, use low impedance scope/probe combinations.

TIPS FOR HIGH VOLTAGE PROBES AND MEASUREMENTS

Rather than resort to the old trick of using a screwdriver to check for high voltage at the caps of horizontal output and HV rectifier tubes—which isn't too reliable—you can do the check a better way. For example, if you simply want to check to see if you have high voltage, you can make a tester using nothing but a small neon lamp and piece of wooden broom handle or dowel rod.

Drill a hole that will accept a neon bulb in the end of a wooden rod about 10 inches long. Next, glue the bulb in the rod with a little epoxy, and you're ready to test. Of course this method is not as accurate as the use of a commercial high voltage probe but, considering the low cost and that you can take it along for quick checks at the customer's home, plus the fact that with a little experience using the tester you can determine the circuit operation by the changes in brightness, it's a fairly good item to have in your tool box.

SUCCESSFUL WAYS TO USE NEON LIGHT BULB TESTERS

If you've been looking for a really simple, low-cost, piece of test gear that will do an amazing amount of checks, probably there is nothing that will fill the bill like a neon lamp. For example, did you know you can check wall switches, fuses, the ground side of a power line fuse box, continuity, leakage current in electrical tools or home appliances, batteries, automobile spark plugs, and even determine if a voltage is AC or DC (and what polarity) with nothing but a simple neon light bulb (Cost? Less than 25c)?

To make a neon light tester, you'll need a current-limiting resistor. The value of this resistor will depend on how large a voltage you want to check. For example, for a maximum of 125 volts a 100 ohm resistor is good. The lowest voltage you can measure is set by the cutoff voltage of the neon tube (usually about 90 volts). At this point, the bulb won't glow. It's easy to increase the level of voltage that can be applied to the tester. Simply increase the resistor value. For instance, a 200 k ohm current-limiting resistor should give you a range from about 90 to 550 volts. After you've made your neon tester, place it across a variable DC power supply and measure the voltage output of the supply as you watch the brightness of the bulb. You can learn, in just a few test runs, to estimate the voltage by watching the brightness. Now if you want to check a spark plug with the engine running, simply attach the tester to the plug under consideration. A bright flash indicates the plug is good and a dim flash means the plug is fouled. See Figure 2-7 for a typical tester.

To check a fuse in any circuit using at least 90 volts (up to 550 volts using a 200 k ohm current limiting resistor), just place the neon light tester across the fuse and, if the fuse is blown, your light

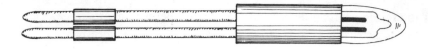

**Figure 2-7: Typical neon lamp
voltage tester**

will glow. A neon light tester also will do a good job of testing for continuity in a power cord or appliance. All you have to do is connect it as shown in Figure 2-8 and if the lamp glows, the cord is good. If not, there is an open in the line or in the equipment under test.

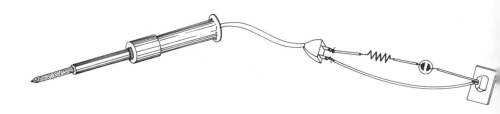

**Figure 2-8: Neon light
continuity check**

HOW TO CONSTRUCT NO-COST
TUBE ADAPTERS

Although tubes have all but disappeared, there are still times we need an inexpensive way to get around the sticky problem of using tubes that have different types of pin arrangements without changing the tube socket in the chassis. Here's a way to beat the problem. Your first step is to remove—*carefully*—the glass envelope and all metal elements from any old burned out tube you happen to have on hand, that will fit into the chassis tube socket.

Next, use your soldering gun and clean all solder from the pins of the cleaned-out tube base. Find a tube socket that will fit the tube you wish to use in place of the one used previously in the equipment and connect it as shown in Figure 2-9.

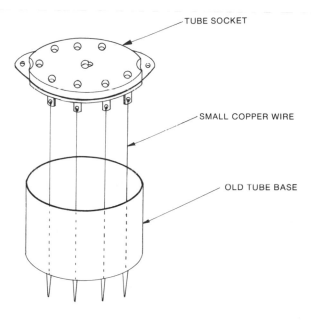

TUBE SOCKET

SMALL COPPER WIRE

OLD TUBE BASE

**Figure 2-9: Exploded view of
a no-cost tube adapter**

The small copper wires shown in Figure 2-9 should be pulled through the old tube base pins until the new tube socket is firmly seated on the old tube base. After the tube socket is seated, resolder each pin and clip off any excess leads. To make the proper pin connections, refer to any manual that lists the two tubes you're working with. I've found, in many cases, that a good book for this job is the Radio Amateur's Handbook, published by the ARRL.

HOW TO MAKE "HOME BREW" OCTAL PLUGS

All of us who work with electronics equipment are constantly looking for money-saving ideas. If you need an octal plug, you don't have to buy it. Why not make your own, using nothing but an old tube base and tube socket? Here's how to do it. First, mount a tube socket on your chassis in the most convenient location. For an example, see Figure 2-10.

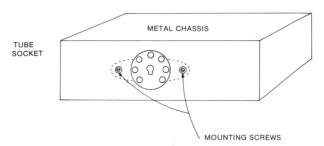

Figure 2-10: Mounting a tube socket for use with octal plugs

After you have the tube socket mounted and all wires connected inside the chassis, take a burned-out tube that will fit the tube socket and remove the glass envelope and metal tube elements. Then clean all solder from each pin. Next, connect the cable's individual wires to the tube base pins by pushing each one through a pin and soldering it. Plug it into the tube socket and the job is done. Incidentally, if you fill the tube base with epoxy cement, you'll relieve the strain on the connections plus have a nicer looking job.

Shop Hints and Shortcuts
That Will Help You Get More
Out of Signal Generators

3

You'll find this chapter to be a practical, everyday aid that will enable you to make fast, effective, and reliable measurements with all types of low-cost signal generators.

Sometimes knowing what to expect when you measure a waveform can be half the battle in successful troubleshooting. For example, certain coupling networks can do startling things to your signal generator's output signal. It's worth your time to take a couple of minutes to find out what can happen—see the section on function generators in this chapter.

Want to know what those log sweeps on an audio sweep generator are trying to tell you? No problem. Simply look it up in the section on audio sweep generators. Or, maybe you want to measure a quartz crystal's frequency, build a "home brew" signal injector, or construct an inexpensive impedance matching network to use with your signal generator. If so, you'll find out all about each of these, plus much more, in this chapter.

UNDERSTANDING AUDIO SWEEP
GENERATORS

Working with an audio sweep generator takes a little getting used to if you've been using the old fashioned point-to-point frequency response measurements. However, once you've mastered the techniques, a sweep generator will certainly improve the accuracy of your measurements and make audio component testing a lot easier. Furthermore, did you know you can test amplifiers, preamplifiers, filters, speakers, microphones, and phase-locked loops, just to name a few, which is especially interesting when you consider how profitable these tests can be?

The first thing you need to know when using an audio sweep generator is what you are seeing when you look at a sweep signal on your scope. We're all familiar with what we will see on a linear sweep, but a log sweep is a bit different. A logarithmic sweep is shown in Figure 3-1.

Referring to Figure 3-1, you'll notice the left side of the sweep shows each cycle opened up. The first few cycles (about the first two) are the base frequencies (about 20 to 200 Hz). The next section of cycles is more compressed up to about the middle of the display. This part is the midrange (200 to 2,000 Hz). Finally, from the

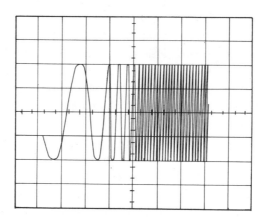

**Figure 3-1: Log sweep as seen
on an oscilloscope**

middle of the display up to the extreme right, is the treble (2 to 20 kHz).

Someone may ask you, "Why not use a linear sweep to check audio equipment?" The answer to this question is that the shape of the response changes when the sweep rate is changed when using a linear sweep, but it will remain essentially the same with a log sweep. Consequently, you can read the display with more accuracy using a log sweep. Figure 3-2 shows a test set-up you can use to test various types of audio equipment.

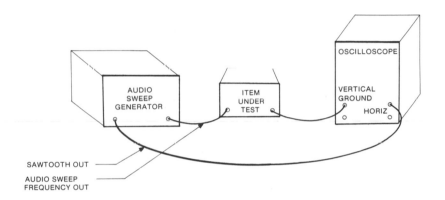

Figure 3-2: Test set-up for checking audio equipment with sweep generator and scope

To make your connections, connect the audio sweep generator's saw-tooth output to the scope's external horizontal sweep terminal with the scope set at external sweep. Next, connect the audio sweep generator's output to the input of the unit you are testing and its output to the vertical input of your scope. While you make the test set-up, don't forget the rules of good grounding and impedance matching. Generally, you won't have problems with impedance matching when working with audio equipment but, if you do, see the section on impedance matching pads in this chapter. It will probably solve your problem. Also, more than likely, you will need to place a terminating resistor across the output of the unit under test. The resistor should be the same value as the output impedance of the equipment under test, if you want a maximum power transfer. However, this isn't always the case. Many amplifiers are designed to produce maximum *undistorted power* into a specific load. A good example of amplifiers that have a load impedance different from the output impedance is solid state amplifiers. Typically, they will work into a dynamic load impedance of 4, 8, or 16 ohms. However, the actual output impedance may be a much lower value, in fact, a few milliohms in some cases. As a general rule, you can't go wrong if you use a terminating resistor that has the same value of resistance as the load impedance normally connected to the amplifier output.

If you're using a slow sweep rate (longer than 100 milliseconds), set your scope horizontal input to DC coupling. If you don't do this, you will probably see a horizontal trace that starts off fast and then slows up as it proceeds across the face of the CRT. In fact, anytime you see this happening, it's an indication that the sweep rate is low and that you should try DC coupling.

Many scopes don't have DC coupling at their external horizontal input. If yours doesn't, you can get around the problem by connecting the scope's external sync to the sweep generator sync output. Doing this causes the scope's time base to be triggered to a new rate each time the sweep generator speed is changed.

Generally, a slow sweep will produce the easiest-to-read scope presentation when working with low frequencies. Usually, it's best to start with a slow sweep and watch your scope as you increase the sweep speed. When you see the scope start to show distortion, reduce the sweep rate until you have the best trace possible. Figure 3-3 shows two scope presentations: (a) is a slow sweep and (b) is a higher sweep rate. Notice that (a) is very easy to read and the half-power points (3 dB) are no trouble to locate. However, (b) is all but impossible to distinguish. It should be fairly obvious that these patterns show a sharp cutoff at the higher frequencies. Therefore, it appears that the item under test is a low-pass filter.

An amplifier will have a response such as shown in Figure 3-4. However, the pattern will change—becoming thinner at the right-

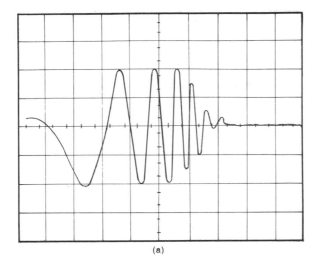

(a)

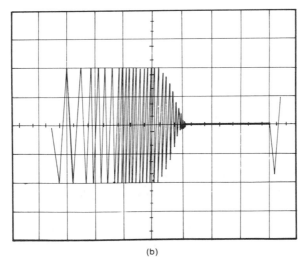

(b)

Figure 3-3: Two scope presentations using different log sweep rates

half of the screen as you increase the signal level. Also, the 3 dB points will become lower, which means you'll have a reduction in high-frequency response. Therefore, you should check an amplifier at several different power points.

As in all testing with signal generators, take care you don't over-drive the amplifier. Also, it's very possible to burn out transistors if you run them at full power for any great length of time. In fact, if they are using a heat sink, it is possible they will be destroyed in *very short periods of time* if the heat sink is not attached. One more point: *Don't forget to use proper terminating resistors. It's usually better to use a carbon rather than a wire wound type.*

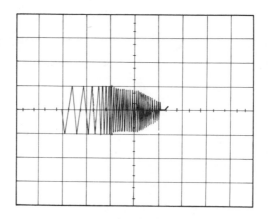

**Figure 3-4: Solid state
amplifier pattern during sweep
generator test**

GUIDE TO CHECKING PHASE-LOCK
LOOPS WITH A SWEEP GENERATOR

Basically, a phase-locked loop (PLL) is made up of a phase detector, filter, DC amplifier, voltage controlled oscillator (VCO) and, typically, is packaged in a single IC. To see how this works, let's assume that the VCO is operating at a frequency fairly close to the PLL's incoming frequency—say the IF frequency of an FM receiver. Now, under these conditions the phase detector will develop an output (called an *error voltage*) whose amplitude will depend on how great the difference is between the VCO frequency and the incoming IF signal. The error voltage is then fed to the VCO, and it will automatically adjust itself until it locks onto the incoming signal. The bandwidth is set by the filter, placed in the error voltage line.

Since PLLs are basically low frequency FM detectors (the error voltage is a copy of the audio signal originally used to modulate the FM transmitter), they are used for FM demodulation. You may find their bandwidth adjusted anywhere from 2% to 10% of the IF and a capacitor and resistor network normally is used to set the VCO near the center frequency. The range over which the PLL will acquire lock is usually set by the filter, and this is called the *capture range*.

Now that the PLL is becoming common place, it's not uncommon to have to check one for proper operation. The sweep generator can make short work of this job and is very informative. The pattern you should see is shown in Figure 3-5.

Here's how to do the job. To begin, what we are going to do is measure the lock and capture range of the loop and set its center frequency. All this can be done by watching the scope presentation, provided that the input signal amplitude is large enough to prevent the loss of lock at the frequency extremes.

To make the set-up, connect your scope test leads to the PLL's audio output leads (for a Signetic 565IC, this is pin 6 and 7). Next, adjust your scope for a 10 kHz sweep across the CRT. When you make this setting, you're placing the center frequency of the presentation at 5 kHz. The reason for this is that all you have to do is count the number of vertical lines on the scope graticule. Each vertical line represents so many kHz. For example, if you count ten vertical lines on the graticule, there is 1 kHz between each line. Now, all you have to do is refer to Figure 3-5, and it is easy to see that all that's necessary is to count the lines on both sides of the center frequency to the points shown and you have the capture and lock range. However, most of these ICs will change their operating conditions with a change of input signal level. Therefore, to determine the system's lock range, you should make the measurements using several different input signal voltages. Also, it may be necessary to use a slow

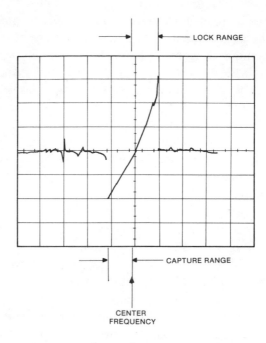

**Figure 3-5: Oscilloscope display
from a swept phase-locked loop
circuit. You are seeing the filter
loop response, FM versus frequency.**

sweep rate during the measurements because some PLL circuits are designed with a slow response to reduce noise.

AN IMPROVED SWEEP GENERATOR
BIRDIE CHECK

This section will concentrate on calibrating a low-cost sweep generator "birdie" marker, used to identify particular points along the viewed trace as seen on a scope. In order to make accurate alignment measurements when aligning FM, TV, and other RF systems, it's critical that the marker frequencies be correct. It is true that some sweepers have crystal-controlled frequencies, for example 4.5 and 10.7 MHz, but many others don't.

Let's say you have one of the older types that uses a VFO that isn't crystal-controlled, and you want to check the frequency of the birdie marker. First, you'll need a crystal-controlled oscillator. If you don't have one, a good place to get a simple oscillator circuit diagram is the Radio Amateur's Handbook. To check the frequency of your oscillator, it's best to use a frequency counter. However, you can zero beat the output of the oscillator against any signal that is known to be correct. Do this for each frequency that interests you.

Now, couple the calibrated sine-wave oscillator to the sweeper mixer. Your next step is to connect the sweeper, oscilloscope, and RF circuit to be swept with test leads (preferably, coax cables). At this point, turn all the equipment on and let it warm up for at least one-half hour. After the system is warmed up, tune your calibrated crystal oscillator to a frequency that falls in the sweeper range and look at the birdie on the scope (you'll actually see two birdies). At the same time, operate the sweeper's VFO to bring the two birdies to a zero beat. Your VFO dial reading should be exactly the same as the output frequency of the crystal of the crystal oscillator. If not, adjust the dial of the sweeper until it is. Lock it down. Your sweeper now is calibrated, and you know it's right.

HOW TO GET THE MOST OUT OF A FUNCTION GENERATOR

When you troubleshoot electronic equipment with a function generator, probably you'll inject the three standard output signals into an RC network more frequently than any other type circuit. Therefore, it stands to reason that it is important to know what these circuits will do to all three waveforms, to get the most out of a function generator. Figure 3-6 shows two RC networks that considerably change the shape of waveforms.

The secret to troubleshooting and what will happen to any of the three signals injected into either of the networks shown is that if you use certain frequency signals from the generator and certain RC time constants, you'll change the actual shape of the waveforms. For example, when you use a square-wave signal with a time period of about 300 microseconds and an integrator circuit with a time

Figure 3-6: RC network hook-ups

constant of about 150 microseconds, you should see a pattern like the one shown in Figure 3-7.

If you set your generator to a sine-wave output with the same time period, you'll see no change in wave shape. This means that during troubleshooting you will get the same wave out of an RC coupled network as you put in, provided the RC time constant is long enough. However, you can lose signal amplitude (right down to nothing) if the time constant is too small. This is most pronounced at low frequencies. Should you have this problem, look for a partially open coupling capacitor, or check to see if one that is too small has been placed in the circuit.

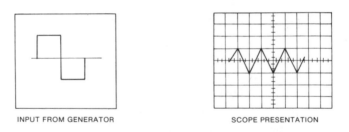

INPUT FROM GENERATOR   SCOPE PRESENTATION

Figure 3-7: Integrator circuit
waveform conversions

If you place a triangular waveform in the differentiator circuit shown in Figure 3-6 and use a frequency of the same time period and same time constant, as explained before, you'll see a scope display as shown in Figure 3-8.

What happened to the signal shown in Figure 3-8 was that the time constant of the coupling circuit was long enough to permit the

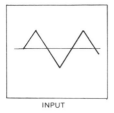

INPUT

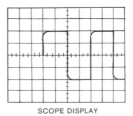

SCOPE DISPLAY

**Figure 3-8: Differentiator circuit
waveform conversions**

capacitor to charge to the applied signal voltage and, therefore, it rounded off the leading edge of the square wave you saw on the scope.

Now, sometimes you'll find the distortion of the wave shapes is intentional and at other times is not. However, during troubleshooting, seeing such a change in signal shape can be quite startling if you aren't aware of what can happen to a signal passing through circuits such as RC networks. You should try different frequencies and values in an RC network with your audio generator and scope to familiarize yourself with the different results. It's not only fun to do, it may save you some time and effort during troubleshooting.

HOW TO IMPROVE YOUR
TROUBLESHOOTING SPEED WITH A
SIGNAL INJECTOR

One of the fastest ways to troubleshoot electronic circuits is to use a signal injector. Besides the fact that it's easy to use, it's also easy to construct. Figure 3-9 shows a signal injector schematic that I stole from the book "Electronic Technicians Handbook of Time Savers and Shortcuts," written by Carl G. Grolle and published by Parker Publishing Co., Inc., West Nyack, N. Y.

You can mount the circuit on a PC board and place it inside a metal cigar holder or similar metal container. To make the ground connection, place the metal holder at ground potential by connecting

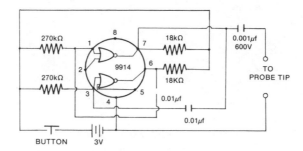

Figure 3-9: Signal injector schematic
Courtesy of ELECTRONIC TECHNICIAN'S HANDBOOK OF TIME SAVERS AND
SHORTCUTS, by Carl G. Grolle. © 1974 by Parker Publishing Company, Inc., Parker
Publishing Company, Inc., West Nyack, New York.

the negative battery terminal to the case. Next, place a metal clip
with a lead wire and alligator clip around the holder as shown in
Figure 3-10.

Referring to Figure 3-10 and starting from the left, the metal
screw acts as a switch. When you press the head of the screw with
your finger, it will compress the spring, permitting the battery to
make contact with the brass screw, which should be firmly mounted
through the insulating material. Connect the negative side of the
circuit to the probe case and the positive side to the metal screw and
you're in business.

When you use the signal injector, the best place to start is the
center point between the output—say, a speaker—and the signal
source (for example, the second detector in a receiver), with power
on. Sometimes this method will cut your troubleshooting time right
in half. If you don't hear a tone coming from the speaker, start
checking stage-by-stage toward the speaker. However, if when you
start at the midpoint, you hear a tone on the speaker, check stage-
by-stage toward the source, using the same rules as explained before.

Try the signal injector when you're troubleshooting AM and
FM radios, tape recorders, and the like. You'll find it convenient,
easy to use, and a real time saver.

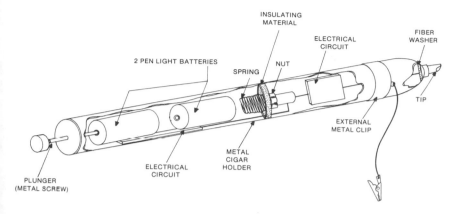

**Figure 3-10: Signal injector
diagram showing construction method**

HOW TO MAKE AN RF SIGNAL
GENERATOR DO DOUBLE DUTY

Go to almost any electronic surplus sales store, and you can
find very inexpensive quartz crystals used in crystal-controlled oscillators. The reason they are low-cost is that they are not a popular
frequency. Or you may have a number of crystals gathering dust in
your spare parts box that could be put back in use.

Your first step is to find out just what the frequency of the
crystal is. You'll find that the markings on the crystal holder may be
quite a bit different from the actual fundamental frequency of the
crystal. To check the crystal frequency, just connect your signal
generator ground lead to your scope ground terminal. The crystal
then is connected between the generator and scope "hot" lead as
shown in Figure 3-11.

When you tune your RF generator to the correct frequency,
you'll see a sine wave suddenly show up on the face of the scope.
Tune the generator above or below the crystal frequency, and you
won't see a wave form anywhere close to the amplitude you'll see at
reasonance. What you have now is an approximate frequency value.

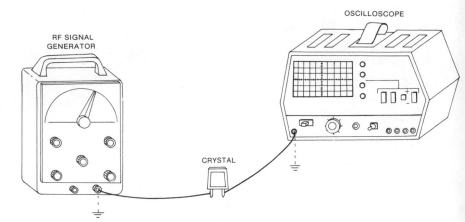

**Figure 3-11: Circuit
set-up for checking a quartz
crystal frequency**

However, you are close enough to the correct value to determine whether you should continue or drop the project. If you find that you're within a few hundred cycles of the desired frequency, your chances for success are excellent.

Now, let's assume you want to use the crystal at a slightly higher frequency than this measured value. We all know that a quartz crystal frequency is determined by its physical dimensions and the thinner the crystal, the higher the frequency. Therefore, our next step is to take the crystal out of its case and grind it down to a thinner slab. Incidentally, you can't do this to many of the high frequency crystals that are sealed in small metal containers or to crystal slabs that are *very* thin to begin with.

To grind the crystal down, I use regular automotive valve grinding compound. Valve grinding compound generally comes in two grades—rough and fine. Use the rough first and then finish off with the fine. The best way to do this is to use a piece of plate glass and polish the crystal an equal number of times on each side by making a figure eight with the compound applied to both sides of the crystal. As you grind down the crystal, keep checking it with the set-up shown in Figure 3-11 until you have the approximate desired frequency. Use a pan of water with dishwashing detergent for cleaning the crystal each time, before placing it back in its holder. Finally, plug the crystal into an oscillator and use a frequency counter to check the operation, or measure its frequency against a known-to-be-good calibrated frequency meter. Then, checking the crystal from time-to-time and using the fine grinding compound, polish it until you have the exact desired frequency.

PROVEN IMPEDANCE MATCHING TECHNIQUES

Many signal generators and other test equipment have an output impedance of approximately 50 ohms. For example, low-cost sine-square-wave generators are typically 5 to 10% off the stated value, which means that although the following impedance matching techniques are not theoretically perfect, they will normally serve you well.

Let's say you want to couple a test signal into a piece of equipment that has some other value of input impedance. You're probably going to have a loss in signal strength and possibly distortion, right? Not necessarily. In fact, if you'll build a simple pad, as shown in Figure 3-12, you will find you lose almost no signal amplitude plus distortion, and phase shift will be at a minimum. The connections between your test equipment will be much more trouble at the higher frequencies than at the lower ones. Therefore, this is

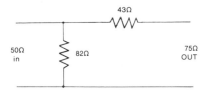

**Figure 3-12: Impedance
matching pad for 50 to 75 ohms**

the area where a matching pad will serve you best.

When you construct the pads, as a rule of thumb, don't use wire-wound resistors. Generally, the small composition ones are better. Also, the reason we choose the 50 to 75 ohm pad is that it's one you will need frequently. Another type you will need from time-to-time is the 50 to 300 ohm. Actually, there are two types of 300 ohm pads you will probably use. These are shown in Figure 3-13.

**Figure 3-13: Impedance
matching pads for 50
to 3000 ohms**

How to Improve
Older Test Equipment

4

Although most of us would like to purchase many of the new pieces of electronic test equipment now on the market, we always seem to run into the problem of not enough money. This means that we have to either live with the problem of using outdated equipment—and the associated lack of performance—or modify our test gear. That is what this chapter is all about—how to improve your elderly test gear and save money at the same time.

IMPROVING THE FREQUENCY
RESPONSE OF A SQUARE-WAVE
GENERATOR

If you have an older square-wave generator, it will more than likely produce a good output signal at the lower audio frequencies. But when you get up into the higher frequencies, you'll probably see something on your scope that looks like a triangular wave bent out of shape. There are several ways you might try to improve the high frequency response (for example, a gate, inverter, or gate **IC** could be used). However, the circuit for one way that isn't expensive or difficult to construct is shown in Figure 4-1.

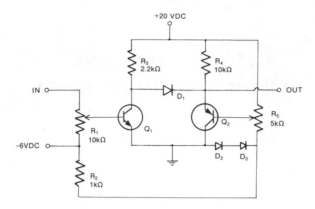

**Figure 4-1: Circuit diagram
for improving a square-wave
generator output signal**

A nice thing about this circuit is that any decent fast logic/HF silicon diodes and transistors that you happen to have on hand can be used. For example, a 1N914 will work well for all three of the diodes shown. The same holds true for the two transistors. You want fast logic/HF silicon switching transistors. With the voltages and components shown, you can use two 2N3638's, HEP-50's, or possibly two 2N718's. The two pots (R_1, R_5) are used to set the symmetry and level of the output signal. However, after you have them set, no further adjustment is needed during normal operation.

KEY STEPS TO CALIBRATING
LOW-COST EQUIPMENT

Calibrating older frequency generating equipment and radio receivers can be a real headache. Building or buying a frequency counter is the best, but not the only, solution. In fact, with the following method, it's possible that you already have on hand the equipment you'll need, because all that is required is a stable radio receiver that tunes across the AM broadcast band. Any small AM radio found around the house will do.

Your first step is to set the AM radio's local oscillator to 1 MHz. Do this by setting the receiver dial reading to 545 kHz. This will cause the receiver's local oscillator to start oscillating at 1 MHz because, as you'll remember, the local oscillator usually will operate at the incoming RF signal plus the intermediate frequency of the receiver. We are using an IF frequency of 455 kHz in this discussion (some receivers have different IF frequencies but the principle is still the same).

Now, let's assume you want to calibrate a signal generator's dial. First, place the AM receiver near the equipment under test—you don't have to make any physical connections—with both pieces of gear turned on. Next, zero beat the signal generator against the AM radio exactly at 1 MHz. Now use the AM radio as a 1 MHz calibrator right on up the dial in 1 MHz steps. If you want to go higher, tune the AM radio to 1545 kHz. This will cause the local oscillator to operate at 2 MHz, giving you 2 MHz steps.

To check the accuracy of your settings, use a short wave receiver that will tune in the U. S. National Bureau of Standards radio station WWV (any amateur radio operator will have one if you don't). After you've made this check, mark the true 1 MHz points on your dial so you can use them during calibration of other equipment.

This same principle of beating one receiver local oscillator against another oscillator applies in all sorts of combinations. For example, you can use an FM receiver that tunes from 88 to 108 MHz. Normally, you'll find the IF frequency of FM receivers to be 10.7 MHz. Therefore, their local oscillators will oscillate between 90.7 and 118.7 MHz. The accuracy of your measurements will depend on how much the receiver local oscillator drifts, how much patience you devote to calibrating the points, and how carefully you read the dial. Your readings won't be exact but they will let you know, with a fair degree of accuracy, how close to correct your signal generator dial readings are.

HOW TO CONSTRUCT A LOW-COST
SCOPE CALIBRATOR

Many of the older oscilloscopes do not have a built-in voltage calibrator. But don't let it worry you because it's very simple to build one using nothing but a couple of zener diodes connected back-to-back and a limiting resistor. A very easy way to do this and produce a square-wave voltage for calibration is shown in Figure 4-2.

The circuit shown in Figure 4-2 will produce a 10 V peak-to-peak square-wave calibrating voltage if you use zeners with a 5 V, 250 milliwatt rating. But remember, whatever type zener you use, the maximum current a particular zener may safely conduct equals its power rating divided by its voltage rating. Thus, a zener rated at 5 V, 250 milliwatts will safely carry a maximum of 50 mA.

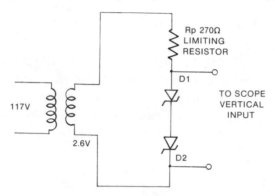

Figure 4-2: A simple circuit that can be used to calibrate the vertical deflection of an oscilloscope

AN INEXPENSIVE AND SIMPLE WAY TO MODULATE RF SIGNAL GENERATORS

Although we all want the best RF generator that we can afford, often we have to compromise when it comes to cost. Furthermore, if you're like me, you're always trying to squeeze a few more years out of your test gear. Sometimes, it's amazing how simple it is to up-date electronics test equipment. For example, all you need to modulate the RF output of a signal generator is four inexpensive diodes and your audio signal generator. You can use 1N60 video detector diodes, or any other type that works up to the RF frequencies of your choice and connect them as shown in Figure 4-3.

After you have the circuit completed, connect your RF and AF generators at the points shown. Next, if you want standard fixed

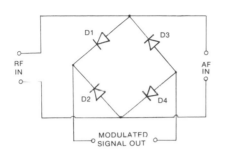

PARTS LIST
D1, D2, D3, D4,
1N60 VIDEO
DECTECTOR
DIODES

**Figure 4-3: Adding a modulator
to an RF signal generator**

modulation, set the audio generator at 1/10 the level of the RF generator. This will produce approximately 30% modulation, which is what most modulated generators use. Better yet, place the output of the circuit on a scope, and you can measure the percent of modulation using the formula

$$\text{modulation } (\%) = \frac{A - B}{A + B} \times 100$$

where A and B are as shown in Figure 4-4.

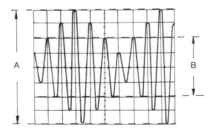

**Figure 4-4: Measuring percent
of modulation with a scope**

ADDING A LOW-COST TRIANGULAR
WAVEFORM GENERATOR TO A SINE
SQUARE-WAVE GENERATOR

Function generators are expensive, right? Not if you turn your sine square-wave generator into one. How? Easy. All you need to make a pretty good triangular wave is the circuit shown in Figure 4-5 connected to your square-wave generator. Set your operating frequency at about 3 kHz, and this should do the trick. One thing you'll notice when you test the circuit is that the amplitude will vary with frequency. Therefore, you'll have to make adjustments during a test run. Also, if you place a load on the triangle-wave generator, it will distort the waveform. So take care that you're working into a high impedance input.

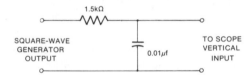

**Figure 4-5: Triangular-wave form
generator**

HOW TO ADD A PRACTICAL TIME
BASE CALIBRATOR TO AN OLDER
SCOPE

A very handy addition to any general purpose scope is a precise reference that you can use to calibrate the sweep frequency time duration which, in turn, will permit you to make accurate measurements of frequency or pulse width of signals such as TV blanking pulses, etc. All you need to do the job is a simple crystal oscillator. Most technicians build their oscillator and use a crystal that has an operating frequency of 100 kHz. The reason for this is that if the scope sweep frequency is set so that one cycle from the crystal oscillator just fills 10 graticule divisions, each division will be exactly 1 MHz which, of course, is equal to one microsecond. Therefore, it's easy to place a signal on the scope (once it is calibrated) and quickly determine its time and frequency. Or set an even 10 cycles on the scope and fill the 10 graticules so that you have 100 kHz, 10 microseconds for each division. Figure 4-6 shows a circuit that you can use to set an accurate time base on your scope, provided the scope has a stable internal sweep oscillator.

The transistor used in Figure 4-6 is manufactured by Motorola Co. However, any equivalent type can be used. For example, a General Electric 2N3663 should work equally well if you happen to have one in your spare parts box.

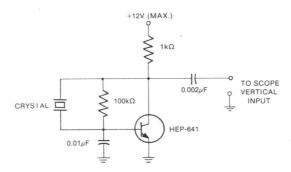

**Figure 4-6: A practical crystal
oscillator for a scope time
base generator**

AN EFFECTIVE PILOT LIGHT MONITOR

Have you ever gone away and come home to find you'd left some piece of electronic equipment on for the entire weekend? It can be very discouraging when this happens. This can be especially bad when you are using electronic equipment that doesn't have a pilot light. I've found that a simple plug-in type night light will eliminate the problem.

There are several types of power line multiple plug-in recepticals (that a night light works well with) that are used to connect different pieces of test gear to the AC main power line. Figure 4-7 shows one type, using a night light for a pilot light.

Some types of electronic gear have auxiliary outlets on their cases. In this case, you can plug a night light into this plug-in. However, be sure that the outlet is controlled by the off-on switch. Sometimes it is not.

Another problem that occurs is that a certain piece of equipment is placed under a work bench and out-of-sight is out-of-mind. By using the set-up shown in Figure 4-7, and always connecting the out-of-sight electronic equipment to one of the auxiliary outlets, you will never leave it on when you close up for the day or leave for vacation. Another trick that comes in handy is to use one of these night lights to check an AC outlet quickly. All you have to do is plug it in, and it will give you an instantaneous indication as to whether the AC circuit is hot or not.

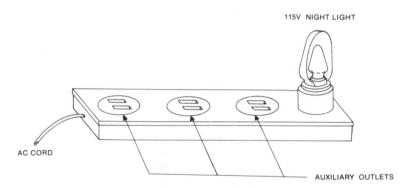

Figure 4-7: A night light serving as an electronic test equipment pilot light

HOW TO CALIBRATE AN AC VOLTMETER

Calibrating AC voltmeters can be an expensive proposition. However, most of us are not about to put out the money needed to purchase a commercial AC standard meter. If you have an AC voltmeter that is in need of calibration (such as the surplus ones you can purchase almost anywhere), it's much less costly to use the following procedures which will beat the high cost of a standard meter and give you a high degree of accuracy as well.

To make the calibration, you'll need a DC meter with good accuracy to check your DC reference voltage. Once your accuracy is established, your first step is to use the DC source voltage and calibrate your scope. The set-up showing how to do this is shown in Figure 4-8.

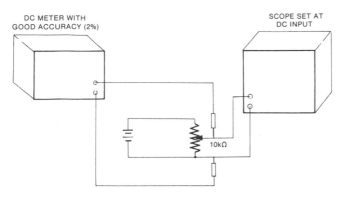

**Figure 4-8: Test circuit for
calibrating a DC voltage on
a scope**

What you want to see on the scope is shown in Figure 4-9. To produce the trace shown, first set your scope to a slow sweep rate—just high enough to eliminate all flicker on the screen—and set the AC-DC input selector switch to the DC position.

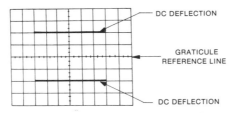

**Figure 4-9: Scope graticule
showing DC calibration lines**

Next, adjust the trace (with no DC applied to the scope's vertical input) until it is exactly on the graticule center reference line. Now place the DC reference voltage on the scope vertical input. Then adjust the scope's attenuator until you have a convenient deflection—say about 2 or 3 centimeters—above and below the reference line. The scope is now ready to calibrate the AC meter.

Let's suppose you have one of those surplus type AC meters with a 10 volt scale and have no idea how accurate the meter is. To check it, simply apply a DC voltage that is equal to the peak-to-peak value of the AC voltage, in other words, 28.28 volts. If you are using some other value, simply use the formula, peak-to-peak voltage = 2.8 × rms value. Now, mark the upper and lower deflection points. Your next step is to leave the scope controls set as is and disconnect the DC circuit and substitute the circuit shown in Figure 4-10. The last step is to adjust the resistor (R_1) for a deflection of exactly the same amplitude as you had with the DC input signal. Your AC meter should now read 10 volts if you have used the same set-up as explained in the preceding part of this section.

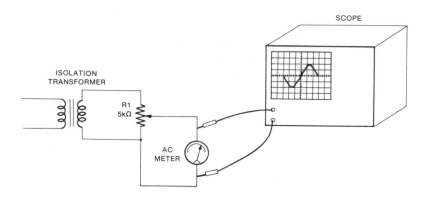

**Figure 4-10: Circuit for
calibrating an AC voltmeter**

NEW JOBS FOR OBSOLETE TUBE
TESTERS

Did you ever run into a troubleshooting problem where you needed a low voltage of some odd value for testing an instrument? A solution to this type problem is to dig that old, obsolete tube tester out of the store room and blow off the dust because it makes an excellent low voltage source. In fact, it can supply a wide range of voltages by merely attaching test leads to the filament terminals of one of the tube sockets and then adjusting the switch to each setting desired.

Another way you can save money and put your tube tester to good use is to use it as a CRT rejuvenator. The only parts you'll need are a CRT socket, about five feet of two-conductor wire and any old tube with an octal base. To start off, place the filament voltage on the cathode and grid number 1. When you do this, grid current will flow during the positive alternation. However, the time of the alternation is short enough to prevent any damage to the CRT. Figure 4-11 gives the idea.

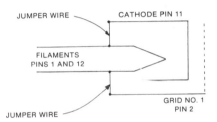

**Figure 4-11: Wiring diagram
for a simple CRT rejuvenator**

To make up a cable harness to use between the tube tester and CRT, use the base of any old octal tube that will fit into one of the sockets on your tube tester. Next, solder the two-wire conductor to the correct terminals on the salvaged CRT socket and run jumpers to the cathode and grid number 1, as shown in Figure 4-12.

After you have the wiring harness constructed, you're ready to try it out. As an example, let's try a 6.3 volt filament picture tube. First, connect the wiring harness between the CRT and the tube tester. Then bring the tube tester filament voltage up to 12.5 volts *leaving it there no more than about 20 seconds.* Then drop it down to 10 volts for 15 or 20 minutes. Very frequently this procedure will put life back into the CRT for quite awhile and, at today's prices, any time at all can be a considerable help.

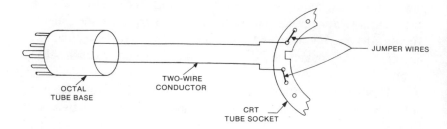

**Figure 4-12: CRT rejuvenator
wiring harness**

You'll notice that we started off by raising the filament voltage 100% for the first 20 seconds and then dropped down to 10 volts, which is a 66% increase, and held it for about 20 minutes. Now, using this same line of thinking, we can rejuvenate almost any CRT. For instance, a CRT having a filament voltage of 12 volts requires 24 volts the first 20 seconds and then about 20 volts for 15 or 20 minutes.

A TIME- AND WORK-SAVING WAY
TO POLISH GLASS METER
WINDOWS

It isn't uncommon to have something rubbed against the glass face of an instrument and have it produce a frosted-glass appearance. With a small amount of care, these spots can be removed. To polish the glass, you can use any mild abrasive such as Bon Ami, either cake or powder, or any similar product, slightly moistened with a little water. Another good polishing agent is a fine valve-grinding compound that can be purchased at most automotive supply stores.

You can use a pencil eraser or soft cloth to polish the spot but, if the spot is very large, this is usually too much work. A faster, and a much easier way is to use an electric drill with a cloth-buffing wheel.

There are a couple of words of caution. One, don't use too much pressure because it's not too hard to accidentally break the glass and two, it's not impossible to end up with the glass worse than it was to begin with. Therefore, for starters, I would advise you first to try polishing any discarded piece of glass you happen to have around. Then, because you are working with glass and a high speed drill, it's advisable to wear gloves, goggles, and a shop apron. Also, *do not* use this procedure to try to polish plastic meter faces. In fact, it's much better to order a new plastic meter face from the manufacturer.

A PRACTICAL GUIDE TO REPAIRING PLASTIC METER CASES

A neat, quick, long-lasting repair of a broken meter case can be made using the method shown in Figure 4-13. All you need is a piece of light cord (window sash cord is good), two dowel sticks (for instance old broom handle pieces), and some household cement such as epoxy. First, cover the plastic case broken edges with the cement. Then loop the case with the cord and twist the sticks.

Next, wipe away any excess cement before it starts to set or you may not be able to remove the cords once the cement dries. Now, place the meter (or its case) out of the way, and let it set for about 24 hours. Generally it's best to place the meter back in its case during the drying time because if you don't, the case may warp out of shape. After you've finished, if you were careful, there should be no evidence of the crack or repair.

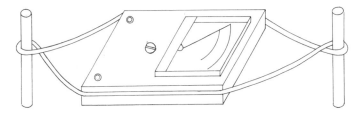

**Figure 4-13: Simple "vise"
for plastic instrument meter
case repair**

Grounding and Test Set-Up Techniques for Low-Cost Test Equipment

5
___

A big problem for many electronics technicians is grounding—especially when using low-cost test equipment. In this chapter you'll find practical and successful ways to ground electronic test gear that will eliminate a lot of grief. For example, you'll find out how to set up low-cost test equipment without the possibility of troublesome ground loops, using nothing but a three-wire to two-wire adapter.

Sometimes knowing a few shop tricks can save the day. For instance, did you know that you can connect two DC power supplies in series and the resulting output will be the sum of the two? Another trick is to connect two ammeters in parallel, and you can measure twice the current you can with one. These are only a few of the many work and money saving ideas presented in the following pages that you can use in your shop.

PROVEN GROUNDING TECHNIQUES

One type of so-called *earth ground* is a metal rod driven into the soil. If you use this method, you must remember that the rod must be driven deep enough to contact a moist layer of earth. Probably a better way is to connect to a cold water pipe (the larger, the better) with copper straps or heavy shielding braid, as close as possible to where it enters the ground. Whichever way you use, keep the bonding strap short—preferably not over three feet. Your straps can be connected to the pipe by welding (brazed) or clamp-on type connectors. However, your connections must be solid so they won't develop a high resistance due to corrosion.

Although I've seen it done, I recommend that you never use a gas pipe for grounding because an insulating bushing is frequently inserted at the gas meter and because the compound normally used for sealing the pipe joints offers a high resistance to current flow. Also, take care there are no plastic sections or joints in your cold water pipe because plastic pipe is being widely used today. If there are, you'll have to bridge over them with a heavy duty wire braid, again making sure you have a good electrical connection that won't develop a high resistance due to corrosion.

While we are talking about things to do and not to do, it's a good time to bring up electrical conduit and wall-socket junction boxes. It isn't advisable to use these outlets because the metal conduit may be connected to several different pieces of equipment that could introduce electrical noise into the system. Furthermore, there are many places in the country where plastic conduit is connected to the wall boxes. It's true that the third (green) conductor normally is connected to ground, but don't bet on it! In fact, in the next section you'll see why it's sometimes recommended you don't use the third wire even if it is ground.

Finally, before you connect a chassis to any type ground such as a cold water pipe, be sure the chassis is not connected in any way to the AC power line. Generally, if there is a power transformer in the circuit, you're okay. However, it's better to check, just to be on the safe side.

An inexpensive way to be absolutely sure you don't connect a hot chassis to ground is to place two capacitors in the ground circuit, as shown in Figure 5-1. The 1 μF capacitor will pass the low frequencies and the 0.001 μF will short the highs.

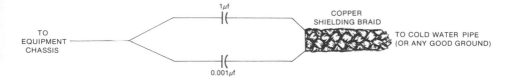

Figure 5-1: Using capacitors to place a chassis at AC ground

AN EASY WAY TO ELIMINATE GROUND LOOPS

It is now a requirement that all portable electrical equipment in the United States and Canada be equipped with a three-pin AC plug, and one of the pins shall be a ground connection. This is excellent right up until the time you use them with several pieces of test gear. Why? Because you may get into trouble with ground loops, as shown in Figure 5-2.

The two grounded pins on the three-pin plugs can cause ground currents to flow through both pieces of equipment and complete a path through earth as shown by the dashed line in Figure 5-2. Because the wire used is not a perfect conductor and may be of varying lengths, differences in potential can, and frequently do, develop between the pieces of equipment. Also, an electrical ground system through earth normally is loaded with noise currents. Therefore, you're going to have noise brought into both the equipment you are testing and your test gear. Furthermore, it's possible these ground currents can set up oscillations and unstable operations that can cause considerable error in your reading, particularly if you are using the millivolt scale of a voltmeter.

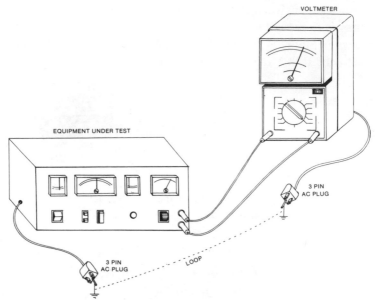

**Figure 5-2: Ground loop caused
by three-pin AC plug and
improper test set-up**

By now you're probably wondering, "How much is this going
to cost me?" Very little. All you have to do to eliminate the problem
is purchase an inexpensive, ungrounded three-pin to two-pin adapter
like the one shown in Figure 5-3.

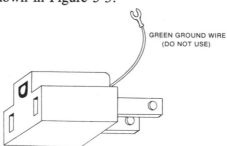

**Figure 5-3: Three-pin to
two-pin ungrounded adapter**

Now, all you have to do is connect the adapter to either of the
three-pin plugs shown in Figure 5-3, and *don't use the green ground*

wire on the adapter because you want to break the ground loop. Using this system may prevent a short circuit to the hot side of the AC line if you use an adapter at both ends.

Another way to beat these ground loop problems is to use an isolation transformer as a power source for test set-ups. Doing this permits you to use a common ground point for all pieces of equipment. However, be sure your common grounding point is a good earth ground such as a cold water metal pipe, copper plate buried in moist earth mixed with rock salt, or a long metal rod driven into moist earth—the deeper the better in most cases.

You may ask, "Why rock salt?" The answer to this lies in the fact that both pure water and dry earth are very good insulators, which is the last thing we want. But since salt releases ions in water, salt water is a good conductor. So mix rock salt with moist earth, and you have good conducting earth. Incidentally, don't place your ground in the family garden plot if you use salt because it's hell on all types of plant life.

HOW TO CALCULATE THE MAXIMUM SAFE CAPACITANCE THAT CAN BE PLACED BETWEEN GROUND AND AC POWER LINES

Many times, for RF grounding purposes, a technician has to place a capacitor between a power line and chassis on a piece of electronic equipment. If you do this, it must be remembered there is a *definite maximum safe value* that can be used. Here's a formula you can use to find this value for any frequency and voltage on a single-phase power line:

$$\text{capacitance } (\mu\text{F}) = \frac{860}{(f)\ (E)}$$

where **f** is the frequency of the power source and **E** is the voltage of the power source.

For example, the value for a typical 115 VAC, 60 Hz, single-phase power line is $860/(60)(115) =$ approximately 0.125 μF. This value will produce about 21,200 ohms of impedance to 60 Hz but only a little over 1 ohm to 1 MHz. It should be pointed out that a smaller value of capacitance can be used. For example, a 0.01 μF capacitor frequently is used for AC line filters. Finally, *all capacitors used on 115 VAC lines should be rated at no less than 400 VDC and certified to be used across power lines*.

PRACTICAL TECHNIQUES FOR RF GROUNDING IN AUDIO EQUIPMENT

If you have an RF transmitter in or near your shop, it can cause havoc in every piece of audio equipment you have every time it's transmitting. Grounding of RF in audio circuits can present untold problems to technicians time after time and doesn't always follow conventional methods of grounding. Usually, what happens is that one part of the audio circuit works as an antenna and another part—such as a transistor or integrated circuit—acts as a rectifier. Of course, once the RF signal is rectified, the following amplifiers will amplify the signal, and it will cause all your measurements to be in error. It also can get into tape recorders and completely mask any signals you're trying to hear on a speaker.

When experiencing this problem, start off by checking all ground connections, solder joints, cables, and capacitors (especially electrolytics). Older electrolytics have a nasty habit of developing a high internal resistance. To check one, try placing a known-to-be-good one in parallel with the suspected one. Pay particular attention to bad solder joints because they can act as detectors. If you find one that looks questionable, it's best to play it safe and resolder it. Also, check your connecting cables to see if any you are using are un-shielded. You'll probably find you have to use shielded cables. If all the above doesn't do the trick, try placing two disc type 0.01 μF capacitors on the output leads to ground as shown in Figure 5-4.

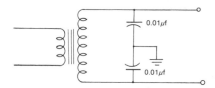

Figure 5-4: Using capacitors to ground RF in audio equipment

Generally, there is little danger when using capacitors to bypass RF to ground in audio equipment. But there is a very slight chance of capacitor loading. Therefore, it doesn't hurt to check for any high frequency blips with your scope. To do this, set the audio equipment gain control at several different levels with a signal applied and watch for any very high frequency audio oscillations on the scope. In some cases, these oscillations can damage equipment such as tweeters in hi-fi systems. If adding the capacitor doesn't work, you can go a step further. If you are working with tube-type equipment, try adding a low pass filter such as the one outlined by the dashed lines in Figure 5-5.

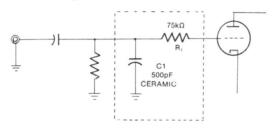

**Figure 5-5: A low pass filter
for tube type audio equipment**

To suppress RF in transistor audio equipment, you can try placing a 250 pF ceramic capacitor between the input lead and ground, as shown in Figure 5-6 (A). Figure 5-6 (B) is a pi-type low

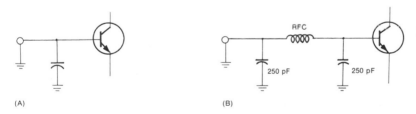

**Figure 5-6: RF suppression
in transistor audio equipment**

pass filter that is more work but better. The RFC value will vary depending on the interference frequency. For example, try an RFC of 6 microhenrys if the interference frequency is between about 30 to 90 MHz and 1.5 microhenry for any frequency from 90 up to about 200 MHz.

It isn't unusual to find that interference is passing from one piece of equipment to the other through the power mains. In some cases, a small capacitor, about 0.1 to 0.5 microfarads, will stop it. If this does not work, try a low pass filter. Figure 5-7 shows one that has been suggested by the EIA (Electronic Industries Association). Important: *Both capacitors should be rated at 400 VDC and certified to be used across power mains.*

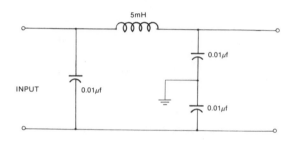

**Figure 5-7: Commercial
power line filter**

HOW TO SOLVE LOW-COST TEST
EQUIPMENT SHIELDING PROBLEMS
QUICKLY

It's easy for RF to get into low-cost test instruments that are in a plastic case, or into a piece of equipment that you're working on that has had a metal plate removed. A quick and inexpensive way to deal with this problem is to use aluminum foil. In the case of an instrument in a plastic case, glue the aluminum foil inside the case, and then place paper over the aluminum to prevent shorting of the electrical components. Make sure you have a good ground connection to the foil and that each piece of foil is well connected to the other. You can do the same job with copper screen, but it takes a lot of work and time. Using foil can reduce the job to minutes.

GROUNDING MICROPHONES AND CONNECTING CABLES

How you ground a microphone and its connecting cable can make or break an entire test set-up. The problem is that if any ground loops are created, it will cause hum frequencies to be introduced into the system, and they'll be amplified just as much as the desired signal. Figure 5-8 shows the only ground you should have.

In this type low-cost hook-up, the audio signal usually is carried on both the center conductor and outer cable sheath, which is

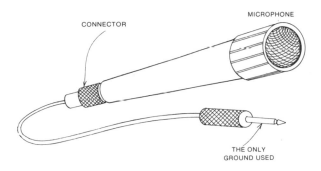

Figure 5-8: Microphone and cable ground point

also the microphone ground wire. Place the points shown in Figure 5-8 at ground potential by connecting them to the cable sheath. This will produce a ground for the microphone when it is mated and connected to the microphone cable. Now, under no circumstances should you connect another ground at the microphone end of the cable or to the microphone itself! If you do, you'll almost certainly set up a ground loop that will introduce noise voltages into the system. In other words, the physical ground is only made at the amplifier end of the cable.

HOW TO MAKE TERMINATING RESISTORS FOR TEST SET-UPS

Many test set-ups require terminating resistors. One example is a dummy antenna when you work on a receiver. The dummy antenna has the same impedance as the antenna. Therefore, the receiver can't tell the difference between them. But the advantage of the dummy load is that it won't pick up external signals. You can make very good terminating resistors to use in your shop by installing a composition resistor of the desired value in a coaxial plug, as shown in Figure 5-9.

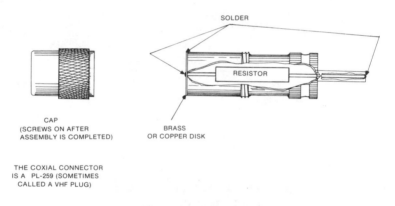

SOLDER

RESISTOR

CAP
(SCREWS ON AFTER
ASSEMBLY IS COMPLETED)

BRASS
OR COPPER DISK

THE COAXIAL CONNECTOR
IS A   PL-259 (SOMETIMES
CALLED A VHF PLUG)

Figure 5-9: Terminating resistor construction details

You should use a composition resistor (not wire-wound). The reason the copper disk is placed on the end is to reduce the lead inductance. It also provides shielding. The power rating of the resistor you choose to use can be as low as 1/2 watt if you're only going to work on receivers and the like. However, if you connect it to higher power equipment, you may end up making a new dummy load in short order. The best way to check a resistor to see if you are exceeding its power rating is to touch the coaxial plug. If it's too hot to touch, the resistor is probably dissipating more power than it's rated for.

The most convenient way to make a high power termination is to use a wire-wound non-inductive resistor. However, you may be able to use a regular wire-wound resistor if you're working with audio equipment. Although it will be somewhat inductive, you probably can get away with it because the error will be slight.

When you use any kind of resistor for a terminating resistor, if you want precise measurements, you'll need to make two measurements of the resistance value. First make the resistance reading with the resistor at normal room temperature. Then place the resistor under load at half its rated power for about five minutes and measure the resistance again. You shouldn't see much change in value. However, the second reading is the one you should use when computing power dissipation with the formula $P = I^2R$. It will also help if you use resistors that are rated at least 50 percent above the power at which you expect the resistor to dissipate. Using higher rated resistors will reduce, considerably, the change in value caused by heating.

THE PROPER WAY TO CONNECT A VOLTMETER AND AMMETER IN THE SAME CIRCUIT

Many technicians believe there is only one way to connect a voltmeter and ammeter in a circuit, or don't think it makes any difference how they are connected. But this is not true. In fact, if the load current is small—say a few milliamperes—your current reading can be incorrect if you place the ammeter before the voltmeter. Figure 5-10 shows how to connect the meters to prevent this from happening.

In some types of low-cost voltmeters, the current drawn by the instrument can be over 1 milliampere. Therefore, if you place the ammeter before the voltmeter, it will read the sum of the voltmeter

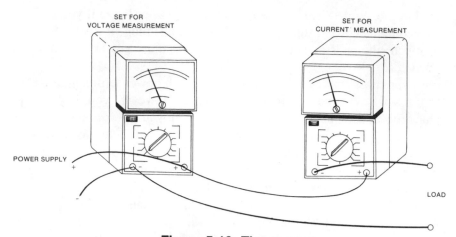

**Figure 5-10: The correct
method of connecting a
voltmeter and ammeter when
the load current is small**

current and load current. If the load current is large, you can connect
your meters as shown in Figure 5-11 because the extra milliampere
or so is of little significance.

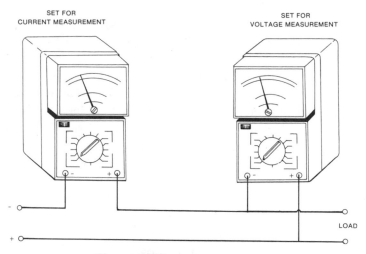

**Figure 5-11: Ammeter and
voltmeter connections for a
large load current**

GUIDELINES FOR CONNECTING
POWER SUPPLIES IN SERIES

Question: What can you do when you need a higher DC voltage than a DC power supply will produce? Answer: Connect two DC power supplies in series. You do this the same way you would hook up two batteries. Figure 5-12 shows the wiring connections for two equal voltage DC power supplies.

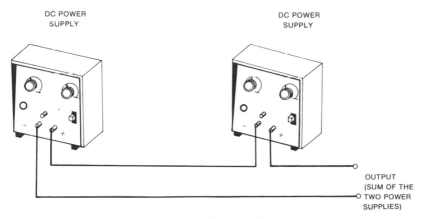

DC POWER
SUPPLY

DC POWER
SUPPLY

OUTPUT
(SUM OF THE
TWO POWER
SUPPLIES)

**Figure 5-12: Wiring diagram
for connecting two equal voltage
power supplies in series**

The power supplies may be regulated, unregulated, or a combination of both. However, if the load you are feeding requires a well regulated voltage, you'll have to check the output. In some cases, you may find the ripple voltage is greater than either of the supplies. A word of caution: *Be sure and remove any grounds because it is possible you could short one of the supplies.* Also, the largest current you can draw will be the current rating of the supply with the lowest current rating.

If the two power supplies don't have the same output voltage or they are regulated, it's possible that the one with the higher output will damage the other, due to voltage reversal. To prevent this, place diodes in the nonconducting direction across the output of each supply, as shown in Figure 5-13. Of course, you must take into consideration the breakdown voltage of the highest voltage supply to ground.

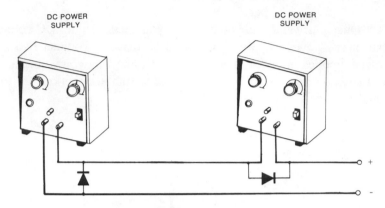

DC POWER
SUPPLY

DC POWER
SUPPLY

○ +

○ −

**Figure 5-13: Two regulated
power supplies with diodes to
prevent voltage reversal**

HOW TO SET UP TWO AMMETERS
TO READ DOUBLE THE CURRENT
OF ONE METER

One of the most aggravating things in the world is to want to measure a current and can't because it's above the range of your ammeter. One solution is to use a precision shunt resistor, but sometimes you don't have one. There's another way to beat the problem—simply place two ammeters in parallel as shown in Figure 5-14.

The maximum current you can measure using this trick is the sum of the full-scale readings of the two ammeters. Each meter will read half the current, so your total current flowing in the circuit will be the sum of the two readings. A word of warning: *The internal resistance of both meters must be the same. Also, never remove one of the meters from the circuit while load current is flowing.* The reason for the last half of this warning is that one of the meters is acting as a shunt for the other and if you remove a meter, you'll subject the one left in the circuit to twice its rated current and, of course, you'll have a meter belching maximum smoke.

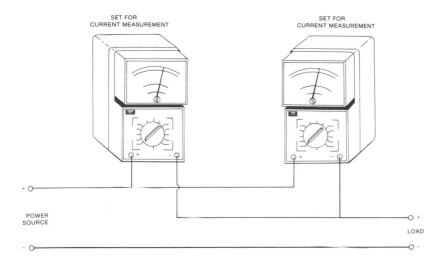

**Figure 5-14: Wiring diagram
for connecting ammeters in
parallel**

CHARACTERISTICS OF MOST FREQUENTLY NEEDED COAXIAL CABLE FOR LOW-COST TEST EQUIPMENT SET-UPS

If you don't know the characteristics of coax cable, it can cause you many problems during testing. For example, the capacitance per foot can change waveshapes. This can be particularly troublesome when working with oscilloscopes. Figure 5-15 shows the most important characteristics of the most often used coax.

Most of the time you'll find the letters RG and some number followed by /U printed every so often on the outside covering of a coaxial cable. The R stands for radio frequency, the number is a government approval number, and the letter U stands for universal specification. For example, a cable marked RG-58C/U translates: radio frequency, government approval number 58C, with a universal specification.

You'll notice that the characteristics of the cables listed in Figure 5-15 include the characteristic impedance in ohms, the capacity per foot and the outer diameter, all of which must be taken

TYPE RG . . . 1/μ	IMP (ohms)	CAP. (pF per ft.)	OUTER DIAM. (inches)	ATTENUATION — dB per 100 ft.					REMARKS
				1 MHz	10 MHz	100 MHz	400 MHz	1000 MHz	
5A	50	29	.328	.16	.66	2.4	5.25	8.8	small, low loss
6A	76	20	.332	.21	.78	2.9	6.5	11.2	IF & video
8	52	29.5	.405	.16	.55	2.0	4.5	8.5	General purpose
9	51	30	.420	.12	.47	1.9	4.4	8.5	General purpose
9A	51	30	.420	.16	.59	2.3	5.2	8.6	Stable attenuation
13	74	20.5	.420	.18	.62	2.2	4.7	8.2	IF
14	52	29.5	.545	.10	.38	1.5	3.5	6.0	rf power
16	52	29.5	.630	....	....	....	....	....	rf power
19	52	29.5	1.120	.04	.17	.68	1.28	3.5	low-loss rf
22AB	95	16	.405	.41	1.3	4.3	8.8	....	twin conductors
23	125	12	.65 x .945	....	.4	1.7	....	....	twin conductors (balanced)
25	48	50	.565	....	....	....	....	....	pulse
26	48	50	.525	....	....	....	....	....	pulse
27	48	50	.675	....	....	....	....	....	pulse
28	48	50	.805	....	....	....	....	....	pulse
33	51	30	.470	....	....	....	....	....	pulse
34	71	21.5	.625	.065	.29	1.3	3.3	6.0	flexible, medium
35	71	21.5	.945	.064	.22	.85	2.3	4.2	low-loss video
41	67.5	27	.425	....	....	....	....	....	special twist
54A	58	26.5	.250	.18	.74	3.1	6.7	11.5	flexible, small
55	53.5	28.5	.206	.36	1.3	4.8	10.4	17.0	flexible, small
57	95	17	.625	.18	.71	3.0	7.3	13.0	twin conductors
58	53.5	30	.195	.38	1.4	5.2	11.2	20.0	general purpose
58A	50	30	.195	.42	1.6	6.2	14.0	24.0	test leads
59B	73	21	.242	.30	1.1	3.8	8.5	14.0	TV lead-in
62	93	13.5	.242	.25	.83	2.7	5.6	9.0	low capacity, small

Figure 5-15: Coaxial cable characteristics

63	125	10	.405	.19	.61	2.0	4.0	6.3	low capacity
64A	48	50	.495	....	....	....	....	....	pulse
65A	950	44	.405	....	....	....	....	....	coax delay line
71B	93	13.5	.250	.25	.83	2.7	5.6	9.0	low capacity, small
108	76	25	.245	....	....	....	....	....	twin conductors
114	185	6.5	.405	....	....	....	....	....	extra flexible
117	50	29	.730	.05	.20	.85	2.0	3.6	teflon & fiber glass
174	50	30	.10	....	....	....	19.0	....	miniature coax
212	52	28.5	.332	.21	.77	2.9	6.5	11.5	small, double braid
213	52	29.5	.405	.16	.55	2.0	4.5	8.5	general purpose
216	75	20.5	.425	.18	.62	2.2	4.7	8.2	video & IF
217	52	29.5	.545	.10	.38	1.5	3.5	6.0	rf power
220	52	29.5	1.120	.04	.17	.68	1.28	3.5	low-loss rf

Figure 5-15 (cont'd.)

into consideration if you're making up oscilloscope test leads. Attenuation per 100 feet is also given for various frequencies. This is particularly important when you're running transmission lines that are to be operated at high frequencies.

To use the chart is very simple. All you have to do is select the size cable, proper impedance, capacitance per foot, and how much attenuation you can tolerate, and then note the RG—/U number. This number is what you ask for at your local electronics dealer. However, as a general rule, coaxial cable and shielded twin lead should be avoided when installing TV antennas because they have a much greater loss factor than the twin lead. The best grade of 300 ohm twin lead insulation is polyethylene because it has lower losses at high frequencies than other flexible plastic materials, and it stands up well when exposed to the weather.

To give you some idea of the losses, a 200 MHz RG 59/U coaxial cable has 5.50 dBs of attenuation per 100 feet, whereas *good grade* polyethylene twin lead has 1.82 dBs attenuation per 100 feet. In addition, the RG 59/U provides an unbalance due to the two different size conductors and has a characteristic impedance of 73 ohms, which means you will have to use an impedance matching transformer. You get away from all these problems by using the 300 ohm twin lead, which is a *balanced* line designed to match the standard TV receiver.

HOW TO SELECT THE CORRECT WIRE SIZE FOR TEST SET-UPS

Before you begin running wires for any type of electronics hook-up, it's necessary to determine what wire size you will need. In almost every case, the size of a wire is measured in circular mils. If you don't know the circular mils of a certain piece of wire, it's easy to find out. Simply measure the diameter in mils (1/1000 of an inch) and square the result. For example, if you measure a bare copper, American Wire Gauge (AWG) number 12, you'll find it is approximately 0.8081 inches in diameter. Now, 0.8081 × 0.8081 equals an area of 6,530 circular mils. You can calculate the correct wire size to use for a certain load by using the formula:

$$\text{circular mils} = \frac{(K)\ (I)\ (2D)}{E}$$

where:

> **K** is a constant called *specific resistance* which is expressed in ohms per unit length per unit area, usually circular mil feet. The value for annealed copper is 10.8 and hard drawn copper, 11.06.
> **D** is the length of the wire, including both wires if you are using two wires.
> **I** is the current in amperes that is required for the load.
> **E** is the required voltage.

Another way to calculate wire size is to use 700 mils per ampere, which is a very generous quantity. For example, number 20 gauge wire that has 1,022 circular mils is regularly used to carry up to 2 or 3 amperes. For larger currents, you can use gauge 18. Using 700 mils per ampere, it comes out that a wire with a gauge of 18 (1,624 circular mils) is rated for a maximum current of 2.32 amperes, but much more current commonly is carried by this gauge wire. The insulation on these wires usually is good up to about 600 volts. However, you'll need better insulation if you have higher voltages. A good source of very high voltage cable—say about 1,000 volts or so—is an automotive store. Just ask for ignition cable or shielded ignition cable, if you prefer.

When you are installing high voltage cable, you should keep all exposed points to an absolute minimum. Really, you shouldn't have any exposed points, but if you do, place them as far out of reach as possible to avoid accidental contact.

HOW TO DETERMINE THE MAXIMUM CURRENT A PC BOARD CAN CARRY SAFELY

Sometimes during test set-ups it is important to know the maximum current the conductors can carry safely. The maximum current a PC board conductor can carry depends on the cross sectional areas, just as it is in ordinary wire. To determine the current value, first measure the width of the conductor with a ruler marked in inches. Next, use the chart shown in Figure 5-16 to find the maximum current value. This chart was constructed assuming the conductors are short enough to have approximately zero resistance and the circuit is operating at normal room temperature.

HOW TO CHECK THE LEAKAGE CURRENT OF LOW-COST TEST EQUIPMENT

To check the leakage current of any piece of low-cost electronic test gear, simply place a 1,000 ohm resistor between the chassis and a good, cold water pipe ground, as shown in Figure 5-17.

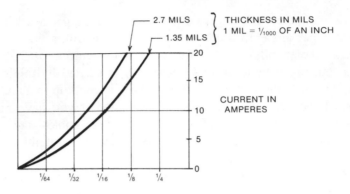

CONDUCTOR WIDTH IN INCHES

**Figure 5-16: Chart for
determining maximum current
for PC board conductors**

Connect the equipment to the AC power line and measure the voltage across the resistor. Next, reverse the line plug and make a second measurement. The leakage current is calculated by using the formula $I = E/R$. If you read 3 or 4 volts on the meter, it's too much. You should not have over a few microamperes. In other words, with an ordinary, low-cost voltmeter, you shouldn't see any voltage reading at all.

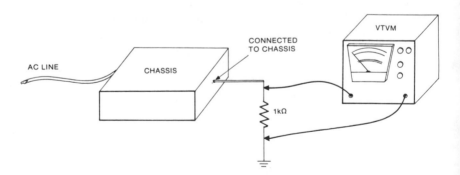

**Figure 5-17: Measurement of
leakage current**

Key Steps to Using a
Low-Cost Curve Tracer

6

This chapter is full of practical suggestions, applications and worthwhile tests that can be made with a low-cost curve tracer. A low-cost curve tracer usually consists of an attachment used with an oscilloscope and can be used to measure almost anything.

In the following pages, you'll find a step-by-step approach to using a curve tracer and you'll see what the curves should look like for many different electronic devices. Every page contains information that will help you get more out of your instruments and provide maximum return on your investment.

UNDERSTANDING A CURVE TRACER

There are several different types of low-cost curve tracers around. One of the simplest is no more than an AC line transformer, transistor socket, and five resistors. It will produce only one curve or a right angle on the scope, and it is frequently a "home brew" type. A slightly more elaborate type you can buy, and one with more controls, also displays right angle curves on the scope when checking transistors. The better types produce a family of curves for the transistor under test. One example of this type is the Heathkit curve tracer.

To use a curve tracer like Heathkit's to check an electronic device, it is important that first you understand what the curve tracer is doing. The curve tracer adaptor draws a graph on your oscilloscope that is a picture of how the output current of whatever you have under test varies with changes of input current (or voltage) and output voltage. You set up the desired input signal and output voltage and then read the scope patterns. The scope presentation reads output current on the vertical axis and output voltage on the horizontal axis. However, a new curve is drawn on the scope for each variation of the input you set up. For example, the display for a bipolar transistor is shown in Figure 6-1.

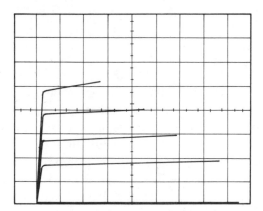

**Figure 6-1: Family of curves
for a bipolar transistor**

Inside the curve tracer there are two sections that produce the curves: the sweep supply and step generator. You set a switch to control the voltage range you want and adjust another control for the correct value of this voltage range. For example, this voltage can be set from 0 to 40 V on the Heathkit curve tracer. Also, you can set a certain step current or step voltage. What happens here is that the step generator in the curve tracer will advance to a higher step each time the sweep voltage completes a cycle, depending on what you have programmed it to do. For example, you might set it at 0.01 or 0.02 milliamperes a step. The Heathkit curve tracer has nine different step currents and five different step voltages.

Another important setting you must make is the current-limiting resistor value. This is to protect the device under test from being subjected to excessive current. Again using Heathkit as an example, it has twelve different resistors ranging from 0 to 1 megohm. Generally speaking, 50 ohms is dangerously low for transistor testing and possibly can damage the device. In fact, a couple hundred ohms can be too low for some transistors.

Two other controls found on many curve tracers are the horizontal and vertical sensitivity. The horizontal sensitivity control is set so that you have a horizontal presentation of certain volts per division on your scope graticule. Next, the vertical sensitivity control is set for certain milliamperes per division on the scope graticule. Now the instrument is ready to test, except for setting the switches for NPN, PNP, and whether you want positive or negative sweep, etc.

PRACTICAL AND SUCCESSFUL WAYS
TO CHECK DIODES

Although a curve tracer can measure the characteristics of transistors, it will work very well on diodes as well as on many other devices. Let's say you want to check a certain silicon diode's forward conduction resistance. Obviously, your first step is to connect the diode to the anode and cathode terminals of the curve tracer.

The next step is to set the series limiting resistor. One-thousand ohms is normally a good place to start if you're checking small signal semiconductor diodes. Now, try about 0.1 volts per centimeter on the horizontal sensitivity and 1 milliampere per centimeter on the vertical sensitivity, and you should see a curve on your scope similar to the one shown in Figure 6-2. You don't need the step generator when checking diodes of any type or other devices with only two terminals such as resistors, neon lamps, capacitors, etc.

You'll find that in most cases a silicon diode requires about 0.6

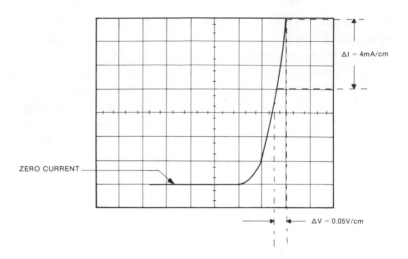

**Figure 6-2: Measuring a silicon
diode current and voltage
change with a curve tracer**

volts forward bias before it begins to conduct, and a germanium one
normally will start at about 0.2 volts. In fact, this is a good rule of
thumb you can use to distinguish one from the other when you're
checking unknown diodes.

To calculate the resistance of the diode during the time of
conductance, start off by selecting a portion of the curve that is as
linear as possible. See the example shown in Figure 6-2. Next,
determine the change in voltage (ΔE) and change in current (ΔI)
between two selected points. As soon as you have these two values,
simply use Ohm's Law to find the resistance. Using the values given
in Figure 6-2, your work should look like this:

$$\mathbf{Rd} = \frac{\mathbf{\Delta V}}{\mathbf{\Delta I}} = \frac{0.05}{0.004} = 12.5$$

As was mentioned in the beginning of this chapter, some curve
tracers produce right angle displays on a scope. If you are using one
of these, a good diode will produce a right angle. It doesn't make
any difference whether the angle is up or down, all you want is an

angle. However, if the vertical part of the trace slants, the diode has too much forward resistance. This is a go or no-go type of check. Incidentally, if you see the horizontal line slant, the diode has too much reverse leakage current.

MEASURING A SMALL SIGNAL DIODE'S PEAK REVERSE VOLTAGE

A small signal diode's peak reverse voltage will vary quite a bit between different types of diodes. For example, the 1N60 will break down at 25 volts, the 1N52A will break down at 85 volts, and the 1N67A at 100 volts. Therefore, sometimes it becomes important to measure a diode's peak reverse voltage before using it as a replacement or in an experiment if you don't know what it is.

To make the measurement, connect the diode to your curve tracer so it is reversed biased. Next, set in a fairly large value of current limiting resistance—say about 10 k ohms. If in doubt, set in 50 k ohms and then drop down a step to 10 k ohms if necessary. Try a horizontal sensitivity setting of 20 and the vertical at 0.5. When you reach the breakdown voltage, if you are checking a silicon-type diode, you'll see a curve like the one shown in Figure 6-3. Gener-

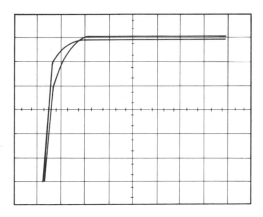

**Figure 6-3: Checking a diode's
peak reverse voltage**

ally speaking, if you're using a typical low-cost curve tracer, you should not see any reverse current before you reach the diode's breakdown voltage. If you do, it's an indication the diode is bad and probably should be thrown away.

HOW TO IDENTIFY
SEMICONDUCTOR DIODES

It's easy to tell whether you have a germanium, silicon, or even a zener diode under test by merely looking at the curve it produces on your scope. Figure 6-4 shows a comparison of the three curves.

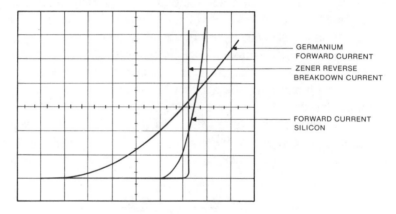

**Figure 6-4: Comparison of
diode characteristic curves
for identification**

GUIDE TO CHECKING
ZENER DIODES

If you have a zener that is acting a little erratically, there's a good chance its internal resistance is too high. Your curve tracer is ideal for checking out this problem. Use exactly the same measurement procedure that was explained for calculating the forward dynamic resistance of an ordinary semiconductor diode. At the point of breakdown, your curve should look like the one shown in Figure 6-5.

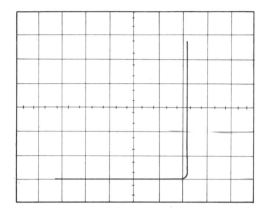

**Figure 6-5: Scope display of a
zener breakdown point**

The ability of a zener diode to stabilize a voltage is dependent upon the conducting internal resistance of the diode, which can be about 1 ohm or less in a low voltage, high power diode. However, the resistance can be as high as 1,000 ohms in a low power, high voltage zener. Therefore, after you've determined the conducting resistance, you should refer to the manufacturer's data on the zener to see if it's operating in its recommended range. Or use a known-to-be-good zener of the same type to make a comparison check.

HOW TO CHECK A TUNNEL DIODE
WITH A LOW-COST CURVE TRACER

You'll find tunnel diodes used in VHF receivers, computers and many other devices. Your curve tracer is excellent for checking these. You won't have any trouble identifying one because the curve looks just like a text book drawing and is shown in Figure 6-6.

When you display the curve of a tunnel diode on your curve tracer, you probably will have a hard time seeing the part of the curve shown as a dashed line in Figure 6-6. This is the so-called

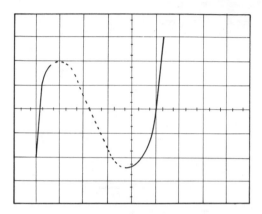

**Figure 6-6: Scope presentation
of a tunnel diode characteristic
curve**

negative resistance region, and you'll be able to detect oscillations if the tunnel diode breaks into oscillation, which it can do. You'll see loops in the curve in the negative resistance region if you have oscillations. In this case, readjust your curve tracer's current limiting resistance and sweep voltage until you get a clean sweep, as shown in Figure 6-6, remembering that you'll have a difficult time seeing the dashed line region.

Now you can measure about every characteristic the tunnel diode has. For example, peak voltage, valley voltage, peak current, and valley current can all be measured. With these readings, you can calculate the resistance at either point or the average resistance by using the differences between the high and low readings.

IDENTIFICATION OF BIPOLAR
TRANSISTORS

A simple method to determine whether a transistor is a **PNP** or **NPN** is to check it on a curve tracer. When making the check, use very low values of sweep voltage and step currents with your steps-per-family control turned about half-way up. Then try the **NPN** and **PNP** position. One way you'll see a straight line on the scope and the other will produce a family of curves. For example, if you try the **NPN** position and it produces a family of curves, the transistor is an **NPN** type.

Be sure and keep your sweep voltage, as well as the base current, turned down to a low value. If your initial settings are too high, you can destroy a transistor in the first few sweeps. If you see the family of curves start to show double lines or tilt up at the ends, it's an indication that you are driving the transistor too hard and it may be damaged.

If you are using a curve tracer (such as a Cobra) that produces a right angle pattern on the scope for a good transistor, you can use this to identify the leads of an unknown transistor. Just hook them up in any order and try the switches. You can get away with this in most cases because, to make testing as safe as possible, most of these type curve tracers limit their maximum test current to a few milliamperes.

If you're lucky, you will see a right angle and, when you change the switch position, it will cause the angle to flip 180°. If this happens, simply identify the transistor by observing the test leads. But if you see a horizontal or vertical line, change two of your test leads and try again for the right angle presentation. You don't care how the angle is presented just so you see an angle. The reason for using the switch for flipping the angle is to check both of the transistor junctions.

HOW TO FIND THE GAIN OF
A TRANSISTOR

One of the easiest and fastest ways to check the gain of a transistor is with a curve tracer. You'll need to know this value to make satisfactory replacements in transistor amplifiers and so forth.

We know that each curve shown on the scope represents a different collector current at a certain voltage. Therefore, if you know the vertical sensitivity per centimeter, it's easy to determine the change in collector current between each curve. This is the first thing you'll need to find the transistor gain. For example, curves 3 and 4 in Figure 6-7 show a change of 1.3 mA, and we'll assume that the step generator is set at 0.01 milliampere per step.

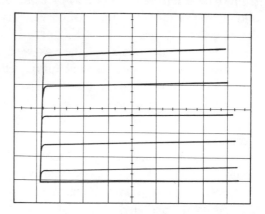

**Figure 6-7: Measuring change
of collector current on a family
of curves**

Now we have all we need because the gain (beta) can be calculated by using the formula $\beta = \Delta I_c / \Delta I_b$. In other words, the beta for this operating point is the ratio of the change in collector current (1.3) to the change in base current (remember we are using 0.01 milliamperes per step). So 1.3/0.01 = 130.

You can check the amplification factor of a triode tube by using voltage steps instead of current steps. The amplification factor of a triode tube is the ratio of the change in plate voltage to the change in grid voltage. Using a curve tracer to measure the amplification factor of a tube or the beta of a transistor is a much better way to do the job because you're using the actual operating voltages and currents. However, at higher frequencies, amplification factor and beta can change considerably, and it's possible that you will lose all gain if the device is used at high enough frequencies. Incidentally, once you know the beta of a transistor, it's no trick at all to calculate the alpha. Simply use the formula alpha = $\beta/(\beta + 1)$.

Another point is that the beta of a transistor is often listed under the heading of **HFE**, and the minimum value for certain small signal type transistors can be found in manufacturer's data as well as such books as the Radio Amateur's Handbook, published by the American Radio Relay League.

Some low-cost curve tracers (for example, the Cobra) have a switch marked *gain* and will produce a horizontal trace that droops at the end of the sweep on the scope. You can get a rough approximation of gain by observing how long the trace is. The longer the trace before the droop, the higher the gain. This works quite well when comparing transistors of the same type.

HOW TO CHECK A TRANSISTOR'S BREAKDOWN VOLTAGE

One way to determine if a transistor can be used safely in a circuit is to connect it to the curve tracer and to use the same collector voltages and currents with the circuit that you'll use with the transistor. Or better yet, check its breakdown voltage. What you'll see on the scope when you reach the breakdown voltage is shown in Figure 6-8. Warning: *When you see this pattern, quickly reduce your voltage or you may lose a transistor.*

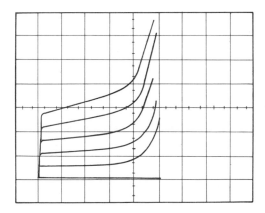

Figure 6-8: Scope presentation when checking a transistor's breakdown voltage

To make the check, simply connect the collector and emitter, or base and emitter, to the curve tracer using the same connections you would with an ordinary diode. In other words, don't connect the third lead of the transistor. Although this is an easy check, it can cause pain if you are not careful. Transistors can get very hot if you drive them hard the way we're doing here. So take care when touching them, or you may end up with severely burned fingers.

Another good rule to follow is: *Always set the sweep voltage to zero before you connect or disconnect any piece of electronic equipment or components to the adapter leads or sockets.* If you always do this, even when you're using low voltages, you won't ever forget to do it when you are using high voltages (up to 200 volts on the Heathkit curve tracer).

HOW TO CHECK TRANSISTOR
LEAKAGE CURRENT

Oftentimes, a transistor leakage current is important to you. There are two ways to check this. One is to check the leakage current between collector-emitter with the base an open circuit, and the other is to check leakage with the base shorted. In either case, you use the same basic procedure.

For the check with base open, merely connect the collector and emitter leads to your curve tracer and leave the base open. Next, increase the sweep voltage value until just before you reach the breakdown voltage. Now you may see one single curve that tilts slightly upward across the scope with a sharp rise at the very end of the sweep, similar to the one shown in Figure 6-9. Generally, the leakage current is very small, and probably you won't see any leakage (the upward tilt or vertical line on some curve tracers) unless you have a magnifier.

HOW TO CHECK FIELD-EFFECT
TRANSISTORS

The field-effect transistor (**FET**) comes in two types, the same as the bipolar transistor (**NPN** and **PNP**). But for the **FET**, they are

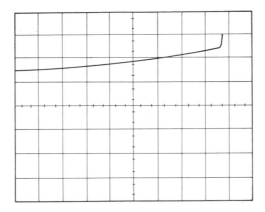

**Figure 6-9: Scope presentation
when measuring leakage
current of a transistor-base
open-if there is significant
leakage**

called *N-channel* and *P-channel*. A very important point is that the **FET** is voltage-operated whereas the bipolar is current-operated. Figure 6-10 shows a typical family of curves for an **FET**.

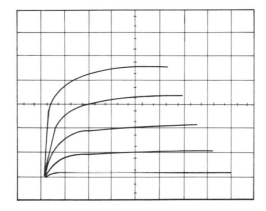

**Figure 6-10: A typical family
of curves for an FET**

The top curve in Figure 6-10 is zero volts from the curve tracer step generator. Each succeeding curve is a step of voltage applied to the gate of the **FET**, depending on what you set the step generator to produce. You can also use a curve tracer to measure the transconductance of a tube (also called *mutual conductance*) by measuring the change of plate current and dividing this value by the change in grid voltage that caused the change in plate current. The symbol used for transconductance is gm, and your answer normally will be in micromhos.

You also can measure the gain of an **FET** in a similar manner, except it is the ratio of change in drain current caused by a change in gate voltage, expressed in micromhos. To make the measurement, read the change of drain current on the vertical axis. Now, since you know what step voltage you have set in, all that's left to do is divide the current reading by the step voltage. It's best to use the middle two curves to determine the change in current because this is about midrange of the **FET**'s operating current. Some curve tracer manufacturers do not recommend that you try to check **IGFET**'s or other **MOS** devices. In any case, be very careful when checking any **MOS** device.

If you insert or remove an **MOSFET** or **CMOSIC** with the power on, it is very likely it will be destroyed. Another fact of life about these devices is that they must be kept in conductive foam (which is usually what they are packed in), or somehow the leads must be shorted. One good way to do this is to wrap aluminum foil around the leads. Note: *Never put* **MOSIC***'s in styrofoam or snow*.

Another trick you can use when testing **MOS** devices is to wrap fine wire around the leads before removing them from the circuit. However, don't unwrap the wire until you have the component mounted in your tester or curve tracer.

How to Get More Out of Low-Cost Dip and Absorption Meters

7
_____

You've probably been told that the classical use of these meters is to measure the resonant frequency of tuned circuits. However, did you know that you can check capacitance, inductance, antennas, transmissions lines, filters and RF chokes, with a dip or absorption type meter?

This chapter explains and discusses practical and time-saving techniques for checking all the above plus much more. Furthermore, the simple techniques outlined are equally applicable to CB rigs, ham gear, radio controlled systems, TV receivers and FM or AM radios.

HOW THE DIP METER WORKS

Modern dip meters (the old name was grid-dip meter) are solid state types using **MOS-FET**s and hot-carrier diodes. Some use bipolar transistors and others use tunnel diodes. But in all cases, they are basically oscillators with plug-in coils for various overlapping frequency bands. They also include some form of meter readout and accurately calibrated tuning control. In most cases, you'll find they are battery powered (generally 9 volts) so you can use them anywhere. Figure 7-1 shows a Heathkit solid state dip meter.

The way they work is to provide RF energy from a tunable oscillator—usually a Colpits type—from which the circuit being checked absorbs energy, when this circuit and the oscillator are tuned to the same frequency and coupled together. You tune the dip meter dial until you see a dip (lowest reading possible). The tuning capacitor dial of the meter then indicates the frequency. You don't need the equipment under test to be energized. All you have to do is place the dip meter plug-in coil close to the component being checked, and tune the meter dial until you get a dip.

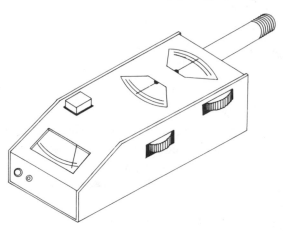

**Figure 7-1: A solid state dip
meter**

HOW TO MEASURE INDUCTANCE
WITH A DIP METER

Suppose you want to know the value of an unknown inductance. It's easy to find with a dip meter, provided you can measure the fundamental resonant frequency when the coil is in parallel with a known capacitor. Here's how you do it. Simply place the dip meter's plug-in coil near the combination of the known capacitor and unknown inductor in parallel, as shown in Figure 7-2. Then, after you measure the resonant frequency of the combination, use the formula:

$$L = \frac{1}{(2\pi)^2 \, (fr)^2 \, (C)}$$

Let's say you have a 100 pF capacitor and measure a frequency of 5 MHz when the capacitor and unknown coil are connected in parallel. Even the simplest pocket calculator can make short work of the problem. Here's what your notes would look like:

$$L = \frac{1}{(2\pi)^2 \, (fr)^2 \, (C)} = \frac{1}{(39.4) \, (25 \times 10^{12}) \, (100 \times 10^{-12})} =$$

$$\frac{1}{98,500} = 10.1 \, \mu h$$

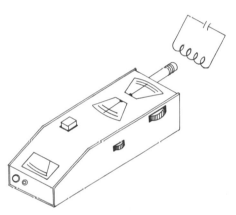

Figure 7-2: Measuring an unknown inductor with a dip meter

HOW TO CHECK THE VALUE OF A CAPACITOR WITH A DIP METER

It's just as simple to measure the value of an unknown capacitor with a dip meter as it is an inductor. Use exactly the same method to measure the frequency as shown in Figure 7-2. Next, swap the positions of L and C in the formula and you're in. Your formula now looks like this:

$$C = \frac{1}{(2\pi)^2 \, (fr)^2 \, (L)}$$

Plug in your values, run it through your pocket calculator, and the mystery is solved in just a few seconds.

HOW TO MEASURE COEFFICIENT
OF COUPLING WITH
A DIP METER

Experimenters, hams, and other designers frequently need to know the coefficient of coupling between two coils. A dip meter and a capacitor you know the value of are all you need for this measurement. An example set-up is shown in Figure 7-3.

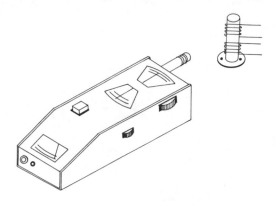

**Figure 7-3: Measuring
coefficient of coupling with
a dip meter**

You must make two inductance measurements: one with one of the coil leads open and the other with them shorted. Connect a capacitor of a known value to one coil and measure its inductance with the other coil open. Then short the terminals of the coil you first left open and again measure the inductance of the other. Now all you need is the formula:

$$K = \sqrt{1 - L_2/L_1}$$

where K is the coefficient of coupling you're looking for, L_1 is the inductance value with the coil open, and L_2 is the inductance value with the coil leads shorted.

If you have two coils wired in series and have used the method just outlined to find their individual values, you can find their total inductance value by using the next formula, provided their mutual inductance fields are aiding.

$$L_t = L_1 + L_2 + 2L_m$$

is used where L_t is their total inductance, L_1, L_2 are the individual coil values and L_m is the mutual inductance between the two coils. Two other formulas that come in handy when working with series inductors are:

$$K = L_m / \sqrt{L_1 L_2} \quad \text{and} \quad L_m = K \sqrt{L_1 L_2}$$

GUIDELINES FOR DESIGNING A QUARTER-WAVE MATCHING TRANSFORMER WITH A DIP METER

Frequently, it's convenient to match a transmission line to some piece of equipment or antenna with a quarter-wave section of transmission line. The hook-up is shown in Figure 7-4.

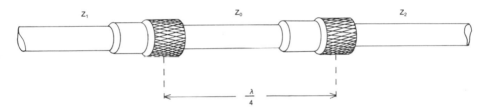

Figure 7-4: Designing a quarter-wave matching transformer

To make the transformer, start by placing the quarter-wave matching section (Z_0) between the two mismatched lines (Z_1, Z_2). But there are two things you need to know before you can do this. One is the characteristic impedance of the quarter-wave section of line (Z_0) and the other is the length of the piece of line you are going to need.

To find the first is easy. Simply use the formula $Z_0 = \sqrt{(Z_1)(Z_2)}$. Now, all you have to do to cut this line to quarter-wavelength is use your dip meter. Here's what you do. Calculate the approximate length using the formula λ ft = $(9.84 \times 10^8)/$ frequency. Your answer will be in feet.

Next, cut off a section of line slightly over this length. Now, leave the far end of the line open and put a 1 or 2 turn coupling coil across the other end. Set your dip meter to the desired frequency. Then start cutting off small sections of the output end of the line until you see a dip. This indicates the line is one-quarter wavelength long at this frequency. The next paragraph tells you how to check if you have exactly one-quarter wavelength *at the fundamental frequency*.

If you want to check or determine the electrical length of a transmission line, you can do it using exactly the same set-up. First, couple the dip meter to the loop and then tune to the *lowest frequency* that will produce a dip on the meter. This is the fundamental frequency at which the line is a quarter-wavelength long. For best accuracy, the coupling between the dip meter and any circuit under test should be as loose as you can use and still produce a discernable dip.

HOW TO MEASURE THE RESONANT
FREQUENCY OF AN ANTENNA WITH
A DIP METER

Pick up your dip meter, couple it to an antenna, measure the frequency, and that's all there is to it. Sounds simple and it is, but there is a tricky thing to watch out for, especially when working with a combination of antenna and transmission line. These circuits may have a series of harmonic responses that you can see on your dip meter, all based on the lowest resonant frequency, and this can really lead you astray. Just remember, keep your coupling as loose as practical and if you're working with a transmitting antenna system, these harmonics (and other parasitic resonances) can cause objectionable interference and, therefore, must be eliminated with traps and/or filters.

Sometimes it may seem impossible to couple your dip meter to the antenna (for example, a long wire type). To check the resonant frequency of a straight wire antenna, use your dip meter and couple it to a 1 or 2 loop coil connected from one end of the antenna to ground, as shown in Figure 7-5.

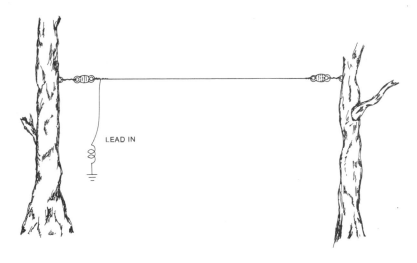

LEAD IN

Figure 7-5: A single straight wire antenna

HOW TO ALIGN A DEAD RECEIVER WITH A DIP METER

Did you ever want to check the alignment of a half-finished receiver kit or check the local oscillator frequency of a battery-operated receiver and didn't have a battery on hand? With a dip meter, you can do these checks with no problem. Here's how it's done.

For example, if you are aligning an IF strip, simply set the dip meter to the correct IF frequency, couple it to the last IF amplifier and adjust the coil slugs (in some cases the adjustment is done with capacitors) for a dip at whatever IF frequency you are working with. Then work your way back to the antenna (if you're checking a complete receiver), checking each stage in the same way. There are three formulas that will be of help when doing this type of work.

They are:

$$L_0 = RF + IF, \quad IF = L_0 - RF \quad RF = L_0 - IF$$

where L_0 is the local oscillator frequency, **IF** is the intermediate frequency and **RF** is the antenna input frequency.

As another example, to adjust the local oscillator of an AM receiver, set the tuning dial to about 1500 kHz. Now, set your dip meter to 1500 kHz-455 kHz (this is assuming the IF is 455 kHz). In other words, set your dip meter to 1045 kHz. Finally, couple your dip meter to the oscillator coil and adjust the coil until you see a dip on your meter. The local oscillator is now tuned to the correct frequency. Incidentally, it's a good idea to check the high and low end of the dial in the same manner to be sure the oscillator will track all the way across the dial. You'll find that most IF transformers are designed to work at either 455 kHz or 262 kHz. The latter type is usually found in solid state radios such as automobile radios.

Since we've brought up car radios, it's a good time to warn you about their IF transformers. A lot of them have been sealed with wax to prevent any shifting of alignment adjustments due to vibration. Now, when you couple your dip meter to the IF and attempt to turn the slug, it's very possible to damage the IF transformer unless you first soften the wax. The easiest way to do this is to heat up a metal rod and transfer enough heat to the slug to soften the wax. Some servicemen use a soldering iron to do the job, but be careful you don't heat it too much if you use this trick. Once you have the wax soft, you can make your adjustments without fear of damage until it cools again.

One other thing. You'll find that sometimes the shields used on IF transformers are exactly the same as those used on the local oscillator coil, so be sure to check this out if you are in doubt.

HOW TO USE A DIP METER
AS A BFO

You can't understand the garbled signals of a single sideband on a receiver without a beat-frequency oscillator, right? Okay, this is true, but you can get around the problem. For example, you can simply couple your dip meter to the receiver antenna and use its output as an external BFO.

First, tune the receiver to the single sideband station. What you'll hear will sound like Donald Duck talking. Next, place your dip meter close to the antenna and tune it up and down until the voice of the single sideband operator becomes as clear as possible, which should be fairly good in most cases.

HOW TO USE A DIP METER AS A MARKER GENERATOR

A sweep generator, when properly used, is an instrument that really helps in TV and FM aligning and tracking checks. It enables you to get a visual indication on your scope of the exact bandpass characteristics of wide band RF and IF stages and takes the guess work out of this type of servicing.

Many sweep generators are nothing more than RF generators in which the frequency indicated by the dial setting is increased and decreased at a certain rate, and these don't include marker generators. A sweep generator without a marker just can't do the job and fulfill the strict requirements encountered in today's TV and FM servicing.

Right now you're probably thinking, "Okay, so I have a sweep generator without a marker and can't use it on today's equipment. What can I do without spending money?" The answer is to use your dip meter. Your next question is probably, "How can I get away with this?" Well, when you realize that a marker generator is nothing more than a single signal generator, it becomes apparent that you can use any signal generator that will tune over the desired range of frequencies.

When you couple a marker generator into the same amplifier stages as the sweep generator, the heterodyning action of the marker generator will cause a pip to appear on the amplifier response curve similar to the one shown in Figure 7-6.

When you use a separate marker such as your dip meter (or any other type), it can be attached to the same point as your sweep generator. But to prevent interaction between the two, usually it's

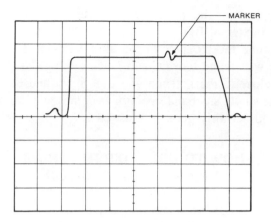

**Figure 7-6: Marker on a
broadband amplifier response
curve**

better to place the marker generator at least a stage ahead of the
sweeper. For example, couple your dip meter to a 2 or 3 turn coil
with one end grounded and the other end coupled through a 0.01 μF
capacitor to the antenna input to a TV receiver, as shown in Figure
7-7.

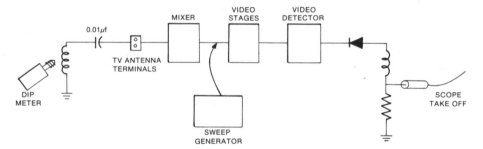

**Figure 7-7: Set-up for video
IF alignment with a dip meter
and sweep generator**

Just a word of caution. Do not directly attach an unbalanced
output lead from any sweep generator or marker generator (such as a
single frequency signal generator) to the unbalanced input of a TV
receiver because the input impedance of the TV receiver is 300
ohms and the signal generator impedance normally is 75 ohms. Of

course, this will cause a serious mismatch. Figure 7-8 shows a circuit you can use to eliminate the problem.

Another point—don't attempt any aligning unless you're sure your dip meter or signal generator is accurate because an inaccurate marker can get you into all kinds of trouble, even making the alignment worse than it was. Believe me, this can cause you to lose a lot of time and may end up being expensive. You can check your equipment by using a known standard such as a crystal oscillator or, if you have a shortwave receiver, check it against WWV.

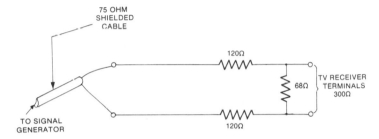

Figure 7-8: Circuit and connections for matching a 75 ohm signal generator to a TV receiver

HOW TO CALIBRATE A DIP METER WITH AN OSCILLATOR

To calibrate a dip meter, you're going to need a high frequency receiver (almost any amateur radio receiver will do). If you have an accurate crystal-controlled oscillator which produces the desired frequencies, couple it to the antenna terminals of the receiver. Now, couple your dip meter to the same point and set it to the frequency of the crystal oscillator. You'll know when the dip meter is near the same frequency as the oscillator because you'll hear a tone on the receiver loudspeaker. Turn the dial of your dip meter in the direction that causes the tone to become lower in pitch. When you reach a zero beat (you will hear no sound at this point), the dip meter is oscillating at exactly the same frequency as the crystal oscillator. If your dip meter dial reads the same frequency, you know it's accurate. Figure 7-9 shows the equipment set-up.

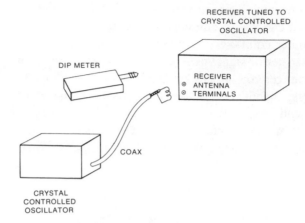

**Figure 7-9: Calibrating a
dip meter against a
crystal-controlled oscillator**

HOW TO CALIBRATE A DIP METER
USING A RADIO STATION

You also can calibrate a dip meter against any shortwave station of known frequency, as shown in Figure 7-10. You can use any station. However, it's a lot of trouble to find several stations when you're calibrating different frequencies of your dip meter. Therefore, it's better to turn to the frequencies broadcast by WWV or

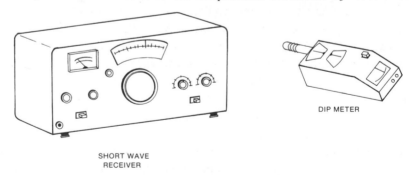

**Figure 7-10: Calibrating a dip
meter against a radio station**

WWVH. Complete information on these National Bureau of Standards stations can be obtained by writing to: Superintendent of Documents, U. S. Government Printing Office, Washington, D. C. 20402. Ask for the NBS Special Publication 236, NBS Frequency and Time Broadcast Services.

Now, to calibrate your dip meter, tune the shortwave receiver to one of WWV's transmitted frequencies—say 2.5 MHz—and loosely couple your dip meter to the receiver antenna terminals. Your dip meter (it must be turned on, of course) dial is then rotated until you here it zero beat against 2.5 MHz. Next, tune the shortwave receiver to the other frequencies of WWV, and you can calibrate at six different points from 2.5 to 25 MHz. Incidentally, if you have trouble identifying WWV on the shortwave receiver, just listen for the voice identification that is given every hour, on the hour, and every half-hour. WWV utilizes a male voice, and WWVH features a female voice to distinguish between the two stations. One last point. Be very sure you use the *fundamental frequency* of the dipper during calibration.

HOW A LOW-COST ABSORPTION WAVEMETER WORKS

The absorption wavemeter is also called an *absorption frequency meter* because its primary use is to measure frequency. In fact, it is the simplest possible frequency meter you can build. Although there are microwave absorption wavemeters that are complex and expensive, manufactured by various companies, we're only interested in the low-cost type. Regardless of the type, they all work on the same principle. That is, they must have at least a small amount of RF power in the circuit under measurement or they won't work.

The basic idea is very simple. All you need is a tuned parallel LC circuit. Hold it near another tuned parallel circuit which is oscillating, and the one you're holding will absorb some of the RF energy and also begin to oscillate, if it's tuned to the correct frequency. Now, if the LC circuit you are holding has a tuning dial calibrated in terms of frequency, you can measure the frequency of the circuit under test.

Generally, a "home brew" type absorption wavemeter isn't very accurate in comparison with any other type frequency meter such as a frequency counter. But don't write it off because it does have the advantage of giving an indication at only one frequency— the one to which you are tuned. One place you can use this to your advantage is when you're tuning a transmitter because it's very easy to tune a transmitter to the second or third harmonic by accident rather than the fundamental frequency you want. To check the frequency, merely tune your absorption wavemeter for the strongest reading you can get. Read the frequency, and that's the frequency your transmitter is tuned to.

HOW TO CONSTRUCT AN
ABSORPTION WAVEMETER

A simple absorption wavemeter circuit is shown in Figure 7-11. You'll notice the L_1 C_1 is nothing but an RF tank with a variable capacitor for tuning. The value of L and C will depend on what frequency range you want to work with. Of course, the old, familiar $fr = 1/2\ \pi\ \sqrt{LC}$ can be used here or, simply use a dip meter to check out any combination you happen to have on hand.

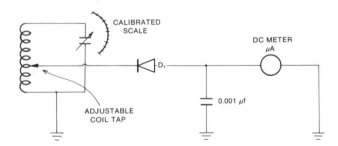

Figure 7-11: "Home brew"
absorption wavemeter circuit

The diode (D_1) can be any high frequency semiconductor diode such as a 1N60. A good place to find a diode you can use is in a scrapped TV chasis video detector. The microammeter is best. However, you can use a milliammeter if it doesn't have a full-scale reading of over a milliampere or so. These meters usually can be found at a reasonable price in electronics surplus stores or can be purchased by mail from the different electronics supply companies that advertise in the back of electronics magazines.

When you are selecting a meter to use, be sure to remember that the sensitivity of the absorption wavemeter depends on the sensitivity of the DC meter you buy. A real cheapy can be made with nothing but a coil, capacitor and pilot light as shown in Figure 7-12. A lamp number 48 or 49[3] with pink bead can be used. They are both rated at 2 volts, 60 mA.

When using the circuit shown in Figure 7-12, simply tune the capacitor until you have the brightest light possible and read the frequency on the dial. If you happen to have an RF microammeter, it will do a much better job than the small light bulb. Just substitute the RF meter for the bulb. To calibrate the circuit and make your scale, simply use a dip meter or signal generator.

Finally, you can use an absorption frequency meter to determine the value of coils and capacitors, using the methods described for a dip meter in the beginning of this chapter. The only difference is that you'll have to apply some form of RF energy to the circuit under test. For example, an RF signal generator can be used. Also, your answers will be only rough approximations in respect to measurements made with more expensive equipment.

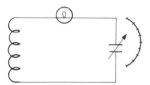

**Figure 7-12: A very inexpensive
absorption wavemeter**

Work-Saving Ideas for Maintaining and Constructing Low-Cost Test Equipment

8

Success as an electronics technician, for business or pleasure, requires a lot of practical know-how. This chapter focuses exclusively on practical ways of repairing and constructing low-cost test gear. You won't find any classroom theory—just down-to-earth ways to repair and improve your test equipment, with some shop tricks thrown in that will save you money.

HOW TO SAVE A BURNED-OUT MULTIMETER

Suppose the light bulb in your refrigerator burns out. You don't call in an electrician, and you don't send it back to the manufacturer. More than likely you change the bulb, and that's all there is to it. The same holds true for your multimeter. If you burn out one of the resistors, replace it. It may be a little more trouble than a refrigerator light bulb, but it's not all that difficult. Let's say you have a current meter shunt resistor burned out and have no idea what its value was. Figure 8-1 shows the basic diagram.

First of all, we know current divides between two resistors in parallel and that's all we have, as shown in the drawing. Next, the meter always has an internal resistance, and it is this resistance that determines the full-scale current through the meter when its rated voltage is applied. Normally, this rated voltage is only a few milli-volts. So take care when applying any voltage to a basic meter movement. Now, to find out what the value of the resistor is, you need to know the internal resistance of the meter.

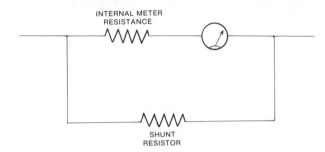

**Figure 8-1: Basic diagram of
a meter shunt**

HOW TO MEASURE A METER'S
INTERNAL RESISTANCE

The following is a fast, painless way to measure a meter's internal resistance. Figure 8-2 shows the circuit connections. First, connect your battery or power supply, R_1, and the meter in series as shown in Figure 8-2. The potentiometer R_1 should be 100 megohms and set at maximum resistance before you connect the power source into the circuit. This setting should be safe enough because using 1.5 volts and 100 megohms, you'll have about 15 μA of current flowing through the meter.

Your next step is to carefully adjust R_1 until you have a full-scale reading. You're now ready to place the potentiometer R_2 in parallel with the meter. This pot should be several thousand ohms and set at maximum resistance to start. Once you have R_2 in the circuit as shown in Figure 8-2, adjust it until the meter reads exactly half-scale.

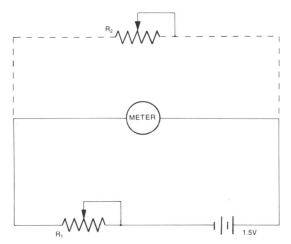

**Figure 8-2: Circuit connections
for measuring internal meter
resistance**

The last step is easy. Simply remove R_2 from the circuit and measure the resistance. Your resistance reading will be the internal resistance of the meter. Incidentally, if you have a resistor decade box, use it in place of R_2, and it will simplify the procedure because you can read the resistance value right off the box dials.

All we need now are a few simple calculations. For example, suppose you have measured the meter resistance and found that it is 50 ohms and the meter current at full-scale measured 1 mA, but the meter range is set to the 10 mA full-scale setting. Now, using Ohm's law, we come up with:

Emeter = (**Imeter**) (**Rmeter**) = (0.001) (50) = 0.05 volts

Next, because the burned resistor was in parallel with the meter, it also had 0.05 volts dropped across it. Your next step is to determine what the current through the shunt resistor is. The answer, in this case, is that it is the difference between the meter current and the meter current range setting. In other words, 10 mA − 1 mA = 9 mA.

The problem's solved because the burned out resistor value can be found by using no more than R = E / I. The value is 0.05 volts / 0.009 amps = 5.55 ohms. Your next step is to make a precision resistor.

HOW TO MAKE A CURRENT
METER SHUNT

You can make a shunt resistor out of salvaged meter resistors, any of the various special types of wire made for this purpose or even copper wire. The best way to be sure that the resistance value is within ± 1% is to use a digital multimeter. The better ones have an accuracy of ± 0.5 to ± 1.5% ± one digit, depending on what range you're using. If you're using wire, the easiest way is to use a copper wire table and determine the resistance per foot. However, if the required resistance is very large, the high resistance per foot wire is best because of the long lengths required.

To determine the smallest size copper wire that will carry the full scale current, you can use the value 62.5 circular mils per 250 mA and be on the safe side. For example, if your shunt resistor must carry 500 mA, you would want a copper wire having a 125 circular mil area.

FACTS AND SHOP HINTS
FOR SERVICING
DIGITAL MULTIMETERS

Like the VOM and its offspring the VTVM, the DMM is the workhorse of most service shops. If your DMM isn't working properly, the quality of your work starts to slide and, in some cases, production comes to a complete halt.

Generally speaking you won't have all that much trouble with a DMM. Why? Because many of them have automatic overload protection, automatic polarity indication, and even internal calibration checks. In the shops where I have worked, we've had more trouble with technicians breaking test leads than damaging the meter. But once in a while we've had to repair a DMM and it wasn't all that difficult, especially when you consider the trouble some color TV receivers can be to repair and troubleshoot.

The first requirement when servicing a DMM is to have a general idea what's inside the case. Figure 8-3 shows a block diagram of a typical DMM. Notice in the block diagram that the dashed

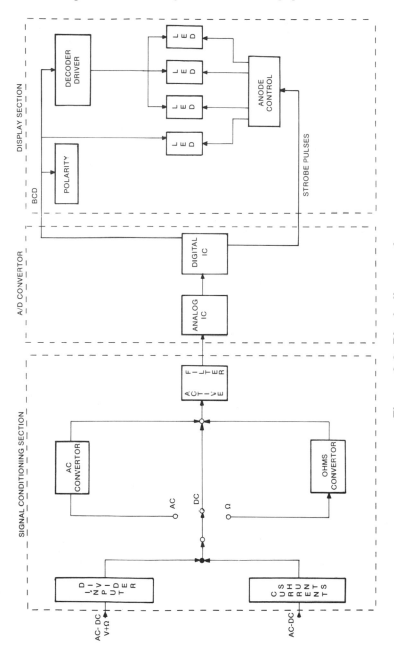

Figure 8-3: Block diagram for a typical DMM

lines have divided the DMM into three major sections. To trouble-shoot a DMM you need to know what each of these sections does.

The section labeled *Signal Conditioning* provides a DC analog voltage (with the same characteristic of the input signal) to the analog-to-digital converter section. The way this is done is by the use of input voltage dividers, current shunts, AC converter, ohms converter, and their associated switching. You'll also find a filter in many DMMs, as shown in Figure 8-3. Its purpose is to insure that the input to the A/D converter receives only DC voltages.

The voltage dividers, current shunts, and switches are just the same as many analog type instruments. Therefore, you shouldn't have any trouble working with these components. Most of the time, all you need to do is watch for broken switches and bad solder joints.

The AC converter, ohms converter, and active filter can be operational amplifiers. For example, that's what the Fluke manufacturing company used in their 8000 A digital multimeter. In these same circuits you'll find **FET**s, conventional bi-polar transistors, solid state diodes, and zener diodes. Again, consulting the manufacturer's maintainance manual, you simply use conventional solid state troubleshooting procedures.

The analog-to-digital converter section changes the DC output voltage from the signal conditioning section to digital information. In almost every instrument this will be done with two **LSI** (Large Scale Integration) circuits and that's what makes up the A/D converter section.

In many cases, the A/D converter uses a voltage to frequency conversion technique. What's happening in this case is the DC voltage at the input of the A/D converter is changed to a frequency by the analog **IC**. The frequency is determined by the amplitude and polarity of the DC input voltage. Counting of the analog **IC** output frequency is done by the digital IC. This count is transfered in **BCD** (binary coded decimal) to the display section.

Isolating your trouble to the A/D converter is very simple. Check for a DC voltage input to the analog **IC** and then use a digital probe to check the output of the digital **IC**. If you have an input and no output, your trouble is in the A/D converter.

The display information from the A/D converter is decoded and visually presented by the display section. The decoded digital information is displayed in a numerical readout either by the **LEDs** (Light Emitting Diodes) or display tubes. The decoder driver is another **IC** that translates the **BCD** information for application to the display tubes or **LEDs**. An example of one **IC** used for this purpose is **IC, TTL, BCD** to 7-seg. (decoder driver).

If you're working with a portable battery operated DMM, there are a couple of words of caution. First, if the instrument contains rechargable batteries such as the Ni-cad type, it should not be stored for extended periods of time without recharging the batteries at least every ninety days. Also, don't try to charge alkaline, zink carbon or mercury batteries in the instrument if it has a charging circuit included because damage may result.

RECOMMENDED TEST EQUIPMENT
FOR SERVICING DMMs

Generally speaking, you should calibrate a DMM once a year if accuracy is important. Table 8-1 is a list of the equipment recommended for calibration, troubleshooting, and performance checks.

EQUIPMENT	USE	TYPICAL SPECIFICATIONS
DC VOLTAGE SOURCE	CALIBRATION PERFORMANCE CHECKS TROUBLESHOOTING	200mV to 1,000 V 0.03%
DC CURRENT SOURCE	CALIBRATION PERFORMANCE CHECKS	200μA to 2A 0.1%
AC VOLTAGE SOURCE	CALIBRATION PERFORMANCE CHECKS	20mV to 1,000V ±0.1% 40 Hz to 10kHz
AC CURRENT SOURCE	PERFORMANCE CHECKS	20mV to 1000V ± 0.2% 10 Hz to 20 kHz
RESISTORS	CALIBRATION	±0.3%
FREQUENCY COUNTER	CALIBRATION	0.1% A VERY GOOD ONE WOULD MEASURE 100 mSEC PULSE WITH 1 μSEC RESOLUTION

Table 8-1: Recommended test equipment for servicing DMMs

MONEY SAVING TRICKS FOR GETTING THE MOST OUT OF SALVAGED TRANSFORMERS

One of the handiest pieces of test gear in any shop is a bench-type power supply. Many technicians construct their own because it's not very hard to do. But transformers are expensive, so you may want to use one of the following ways to beat this problem.

Go to almost any surplus electronics store, and you can find tube type transformers that are very inexpensive. After all, who wants a 6 volt filament transformer anymore? What we need today are 9 and 12 volt transformers, right? Not necessarily. For example, connect two center tapped 6 volt transformers as shown in Figure 8-4, and you'll have a 3, 6, 9 and 12 volt output.

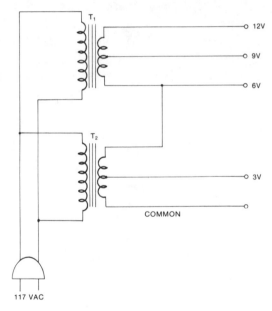

Figure 8-4: Wiring diagram for obtaining a 3, 6, 9 and 12 volt output from two 6 volt center tapped transformers

Another trick you can use when building power supplies is to parallel two transformers for double the current output that one would handle. If both transformers are identical, you probably won't have any trouble. However, if you're in doubt, apply power with no load and let the transformers sit for about an hour or so. Then touch them to see if they are overheating. Figure 8-5 shows the wiring hook-up.

Before you connect the two transformers in parallel as shown in Figure 8-5, *it's very important that you check the phasing polarity of each transformer if you're not sure about it.* Just recently, a technician showed me a simple way to determine the phase polarity of an unknown transformer. Here's what he did. He placed a voltage on the primary (if the transformer is a power transformer and color coded, the primary leads are usually the black ones) and measured the primary voltage with an AC voltmeter. Next, he connected a

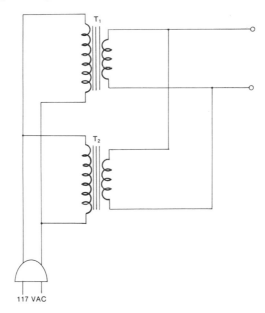

Figure 8-5: Paralleling two transformers for double the current of one

jumper lead from lead 1 to lead 3, as shown in Figure 8-6. Then he measured the voltage between leads 2 and 4. Here's the secret. If the voltage you measured on the primary leads is higher than the second measured voltage, lead 1 has the same polarity as lead 3. If the primary voltage is lower, lead 3 has the same polarity as lead 2.

Can you connect two transformers with different output voltages together? Sure can. In fact, doing this can produce several different voltages depending on whether the transformers are center tapped and how you hook them up. For example, connect the

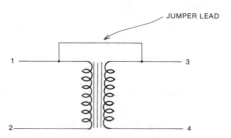

Figure 8-6: Checking a transformer phasing polarity

primaries in parallel and their secondaries in series as shown in Figure 8-7, and you'll have the sum of the two output voltages.

Another way to connect transformers to get odd-ball voltages is to connect the primaries in parallel and reverse the secondary leads

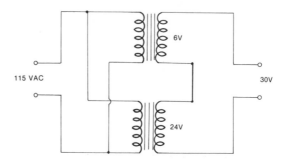

Figure 8-7: Using two transformers to develop a higher output voltage

shown in Figure 8-7 to the connections shown in Figure 8-8. However, we're assuming, in this case, you're using a center tapped 6 V transformer.

When using any of these various transformer wiring hook-ups, it is important to remember that the maximum current the load can draw is set by the transformer with the *lowest current rating*. If you don't know the current rating of a transformer, connect the maximum load and measure the temperature with a thermometer. Before hooking any load to the transformer, let it warm up for about an hour without a load and then measure its temperature.

Next, place the full load on the transformer and let it run about another hour (checking the thermometer periodically). You should not have a temperature rise of more than 68°F (20°C) to 86°F (30°C) at anytime during the hour. For smaller transformers, use the 68°F temperature rise value and on larger transformers, the 86°F value.

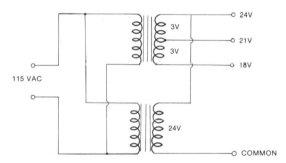

**Figure 8-8: Connecting two
transformers so one will buck
the voltage of the other**

A SIMPLE WAY TO MAKE
YOUR SCOPE MEASURE
ALMOST ANYTHING

How would you like a circuit you can build with junk box parts in just a few minutes that will do all the following (when used with your scope), and not have to have the equipment under test energized?

1. Indicate shorts and open circuits.
2. Measure approximate resistance values.
3. Measure approximate capacitance values.
4. Measure approximate inductance values.
5. Check diodes.
6. Check transistors.
7. Determine whether a diode is a germanium or silicon type.
8. Determine whether a transistor is a germanium or silicon type and which lead is the base lead.

You can do all this and more (depending on how good you get at analyzing the scope display), using the circuit shown in Figure 8-9. The story of this circuit is similar to the story of glass. The Egyptians discovered the secret of making glass about 3,000 years ago, but it was lost for 1,000 years before it was discovered again. The circuit shown in Figure 8-9 was popular in the 1930's, but was almost forgotten until the 1970's when it again became popular because it's so inexpensive and excellent for troubleshooting.

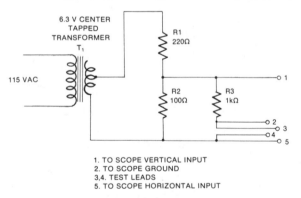

Figure 8-9: Schematic of a test circuit that, when used with a scope, will test almost anything

Notice that all you need is one surplus 6.3 volt center tapped filament transformer and three resistors which you probably have in your junk box. The wattage rating of the resistors is not critical.

One-half watt or more is fine because, as you can see, the applied voltage from the transformer is only about 3 volts.

The resistors R_1 and R_2 are nothing more than a voltage divider network that will produce about 1 volt AC between the two resistors. You will apply this voltage to any component when you connect the test leads across it. The voltage across the probes will be applied to your scope's horizontal input and the voltage across R_3 (this will depend on your load current) is applied to the scope's vertical input. In other words, the display on the scope is voltage VS current of the component under test.

Now, looking at the schematic, you should be able to see that if the test leads are open the only thing being applied to the scope is a horizontal signal because we're not getting any current through resistor R_3. Therefore, to calibrate the horizontal line on your scope, simply set the length of the horizontal line to some convenient value by adjusting the scope's horizontal gain control. Figure 8-10 shows what you should see on your scope after the horizontal is adjusted.

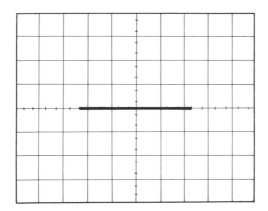

**Figure 8-10: Horizontal scope
calibration**

Your next step is to calibrate the vertical. To do this, merely short the test leads and then adjust the vertical line that you'll see, to the same length you choose for the horizontal line. What you'll see on the scope screen is shown in Figure 8-11.

Once you have the scope calibrated, your next step is to learn how to read the scope presentation. For example, we said that you could read approximate resistance values, which is a tremendous help for fast troubleshooting. To learn to do this, simply pick up a handful of resistors; any values will do. Of course, the values that you normally encounter when troubleshooting in your daily work are the best to use.

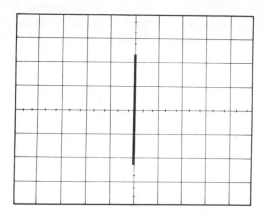

Figure 8-11: Vertical scope calibration

What you'll see on your scope will depend on the resistance you measure. For instance, if the resistance value is small, your scope will show you a single line almost vertical. On the other hand, if the resistor has a much larger value, you'll see an almost horizontal line. A resistor half-way between will produce a slanting line somewhere between a vertical and horizontal line. Figure 8-12 shows several possible traces. Once you're familiar with what a certain resistance value will produce on the scope, it's no trick at all to rapidly read approximate resistance values during troubleshooting.

To check the approximate value of a capacitor is just as simple as checking resistors. Here, again, you need a handful of components to familiarize yourself with the scope presentation for different values of capacitors. Because the test circuit is basically a phase shifting network, you'll see an ellipse or circle on the scope when

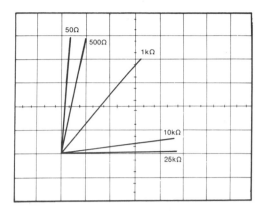

**Figure 8-12: Possible scope
presentations you'll see when
measuring resistance**

you place your test leads across a capacitor or inductor. A small capacitance will produce a very flat horizontal ellipse, and a large value will produce a thin vertical ellipse. Figure 8-13 shows a couple of patterns you may see on the scope.

If you place a capacitor having the same reactance value as the resistor R_3, you'll produce a circle on the scope. We know that R_3 is

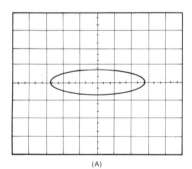

(A)

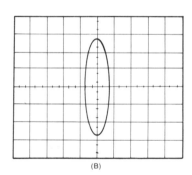

(B)

**Figure 8-13: Scope
presentation when measuring
capacitance. (A) indicates a
small value (0.01 μF) and (B)
indicates a large value (50 μF)**

1,000 ohms. So it's easy to calculate the capacitance value you need. Simply use the formula $C = 1 / 2 \pi F XC$ and it comes out that a 2.65 μF capacitor should do the job. Like measuring resistance, with a little practice you can get pretty good at estimating the value of a capacitor, which, in most cases, is about all you need when troubleshooting. Next, do the same thing with known values of inductance, and you can learn to read them in the same way you did capacitors and resistors.

How about diodes? No problem. You'll see one of the scope presentations shown in Figure 8-14. Which one you see will depend on how you connect the test leads to the diode. Whichever one you get, reverse the test leads, and you'll get the other. It doesn't really matter which presentation you get while troubleshooting. Just as long as you see a good right angle, it's an indication the diode is good.

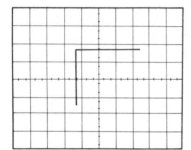 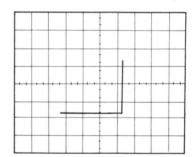

**Figure 8-14: Scope
presentation indicating a
good diode**

You can tell if the diode is a germanium or silicon type by the length of the horizontal line. Try a couple, and you'll see that the horizontal line for the silicon diode is longer than the vertical line, which is a dead give away when trying to determine what type diode you have.

Let's say you have a few unknown capacitors you want to check. We've already explained how to check for a go or no go and estimate the value, but it's also important to know if a capacitor is leaky. Figure 8-15 shows what you'll see on the scope, in this case. Notice that the angle isn't a right angle. This is an indication that the capacitor is bad. During troubleshooting, if you see only one vertical line, it's an indication that you have a short. A single horizontal line means an open circuit.

Finally, what about transistors? To check transistor junctions, use exactly the same procedure as for diodes. You'll see the same patterns as shown in Figure 8-14, and the same rules hold true for determining whether it is a silicon or germanium type. If the transistor has a leaky junction, you'll see the pattern shown in Figure 8-15. To identify the base on a transistor, touch one of the transistor leads with the test lead coming off the scope's horizontal input lead (shown in Figure 8-9). Next, touch the other lead to each of the

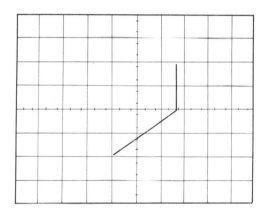

**Figure 8-15: Scope
presentation of a faulty capacitor**

other two transistor leads. When you find the base lead, you'll get almost identical scope presentations when you touch the test lead to the other two transistor leads.

We could go on for pages about all the tests you can make with this simple circuit. But the real secret is that all you have to do is place the test leads across any known-to-be good circuit or component and, once you know a correct presentation, you're in because any change indicates trouble. The beautiful thing about this is that no power is required to be fed to the component or equipment under test. What this means is you can simulate troubles without damaging anything. For example, add resistance, capacitance, or series capacitance, etc. and see what happens to your scope pattern. As we've said before, with a little experimenting you can learn to troubleshoot almost anything with this simple test instrument and, best of all, it doesn't cost a fortune to build.

Practical Ways to Get More Out of Low-Cost Oscilloscopes

9

This chapter contains simple procedures that reduce some of the trickiest testing jobs to interesting and accurate checks. For example: how to measure attenuation quickly and inexpensively, how to check a TV receiver chassis in minutes, and how to measure high frequency voltage with an accuracy far above ordinary meters. You'll also find proven techniques for checking rise time and linearity that are critical for determining how a low-cost scope will perform during circuit testing. All these techniques and more are designed to show you how to turn out superior work with an oscilloscope.

MEASURING ATTENUATION QUICKLY AND ACCURATELY WITH YOUR SCOPE

A practical technique we all need from time to time is how to measure attenuation in decibels (dBs) between two points on a certain waveform. An easy way to do this is to make the scale described, place it on your scope, and read dBs straight off the graticule.

The graticule shown in Figure 9-1 is a standard scale. In other words, there are eight vertical and ten horizontal centimeter graduations. Notice that each vertical centimeter graduation has been subdivided into two divisions. However, you can use more or less divisions depending on your needs, as you will see.

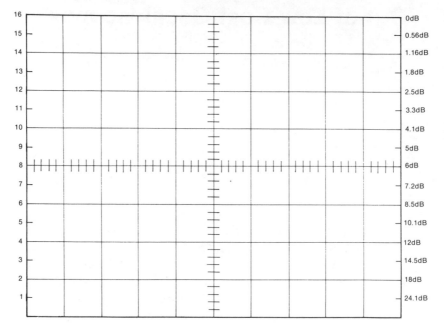

**Figure 9-1: A handy dB scale
for an oscilloscope**

When constructing the scale, simply use the formula dB = 20 log (division$_1$/division$_2$). In this case, division 1 will always be 16 because we want to measure attenuation, and the top of the scale (a total of 16 divisions) is our reference. For example, with a calculator that does logs, you can calculate the 6 dB attenuation point as follows:

$$dB = 20 \log 16/8 = 6 \text{ dB}$$

Now, do this for each of the 16 points—or as many as you like—and your scale should look similar to the one shown in Figure 9-1. If you don't have an engineering type calculator, merely trace Figure 9-1 on a piece of plastic, place it on the face of your scope, and it will give you reasonable accuracy.

Once you have the scale made, here's how to use it. Let's assume you're using a sweep generator and doing a wideband alignment. First, the scope controls must be set so the display exactly fills the screen as shown in Figure 9-2. Next, to determine the amount of attenuation at some predetermined point on the waveform, simply locate the point you want and read it on the right-hand scale. Your answer will be in dB below the peak voltage.

Finally, a brief note of warning: Be sure you *don't overdrive your scope amplifiers* because, if you do, it will flatten the waveform and probably cause errors in your reading. Also, if you are working on bandpass alignment, you should remember that *6 dB = 50% of peak voltage*, not 3 dB as with a power ratio. The reason is that the number of decibels corresponding to a given *power ratio* is given by dB $= 10\log P_2/P_1$. Therefore, 3 dB $= 50\%$ of peak power (P_2).

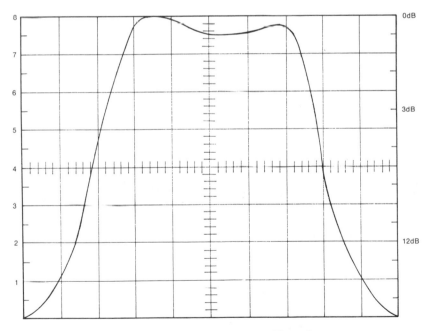

Figure 9-2: Measuring dBs of attenuation with an oscilloscope

HOW A SCOPE CAN HELP YOU
WORK ON POWER SUPPLIES

One of the best ways to check a power supply is with an oscilloscope—especially regulated supplies. We all know that an open filter capacitor or one that is low in value can cause excessive ripple. To check for ripple, set your scope to an AC signal input and use a high sensitivity position on your vertical input attenuator. Figure 9-3 shows a schematic diagram of a typical low-cost variable output DC power supply.

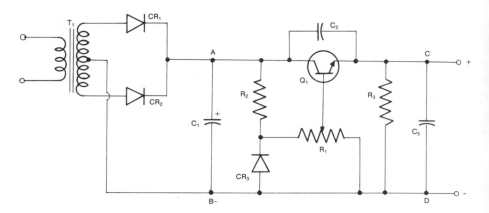

Figure 9-3: Low voltage,
variable output DC power supply

When checking the filter capacitor (C_1 or C_3), place the scope probes at points A and B or C and D as shown in the schematic in Figure 9-3. If you see a waveform as shown in Figure 9-4(A), the filter capacitor is probably open. However, if you see a waveform as shown in Figure 9-4 (B), the filter capacitor is working properly.

If the power supply you want to check has a built-in voltage regulator, it's easy to determine when the regulator can't handle the voltage variations. All you have to do is look at the power supply output and input to the voltage regulator circuit. At the same time, it's a good idea to watch for any oscillations or spikes that may be present, especially when working with digital equipment. If you should run into problems, two things that could cause oscillations (motor boating) in a regulated power supply are: (1) A faulty by-pass capacitor and, (2) a large reactive load.

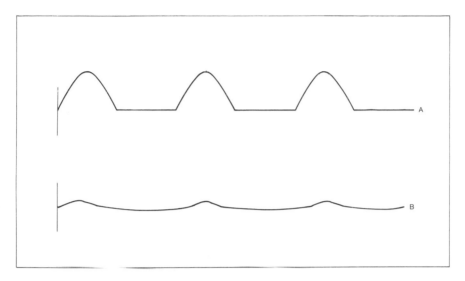

**Figure 9-4: Proper and
improper filter capacitor
waveforms**

HOW TO AVOID ERRORS WHEN
USING A SCOPE

Although the oscilloscope is one of the most versatile electronic instruments in any shop, it is also one of the most troublesome to operate properly. For example, take the case of a simple coax cable lead. Many technicians are not aware that some coax cables have as much as 30 pico farads per foot. Doesn't sound like much, right? Well, don't you believe it because there's more than meets the eye!

To begin, we normally use cables of 3 feet and it isn't unusual to connect 3 sections together to make up a vertical input lead. Now, considering the fact that some scopes have input capacitances of 40 pico farads, it's possible to end up with about 310 pico farads with just the 3 sections of cable. What this boils down to is that on low impedance circuits you're okay, but you can get very heavy circuit loading as you increase your test frequency. This is one of the reasons why every text book states: "Keep all leads short when working with high frequencies." Incidentally, you can get high frequency compensated scope probes with 10 megohm, 11.5 pico farad input impedance, × 10 attenuation, that should be used with your scope when working with TV frequencies. Remember, always check the attenuation on the scope probe. Normally, it should be × 10 and the attenuation ratio will be found on the attenuator as shown in Figure 9-5.

A couple of common errors when using a scope are: (1) The technician forgets to include probe attenuation when making amplitude measurements, or (2) he doesn't check to see if the scope has a wide enough bandwidth. For example, if you are analyzing logic circuits, it's easy to miss a narrow pulse that is causing the trouble if your scope's bandwidth is too low.

**Figure 9-5: Attenuation of a
scope probe**

CHECKING YOUR SCOPE FOR
DIGITAL WORK

All of us working in the field of electronics are forever trying to get more out of our test equipment. One of the big questions is, "How will my scope perform when making measurements in digital circuits?" You can answer this by checking the rise time of your scope. To do this, you must first find the upper frequency at which your scope is 3 dB down. If you have the manual that came with the scope, this information is probably in it. However, if you don't, it isn't hard to check.

If you have made the dB scale for your scope as explained in the first section of this chapter (see Figure 9-1), simply apply a signal to your scope and fill the graticule. Next, raise the input frequency until the display is reduced to the 3 dB point or, if you raise the frequency until the display is reduced by about 30%, it will be approximately the 3 dB point.

Now let's assume that your scope has a band-pass of about 10 MHz at the 3 dB point. Your next step is to calculate the period with the formula, period = 1 / frequency. This comes out 0.1 microsecond, and you have only one-third of this at the 3 dB point. So this works out to be 33.3 pico seconds, and means the scope will display a rise time of 33.3 pico seconds.

Let's take another example. Assume a scope has a band-pass of 4 MHz at 3 dB down. In this case we get 0.2 microseconds, and a third of this is 0.06 microseconds. In other words, this scope can't perform as well as the 10 MHZ band-bass one we first discussed.

It should be pointed out that although low-cost electronic test equipment manufacturers have made remarkable improvements in their instruments' performance, RF signal generators in this category will not have an output signal with a relatively flat response (± 0.5 dB) over the test frequencies described. Therefore, due to this fact and because we're working with complex waveforms, your readings will only be rough approximations using this procedure.

GUIDELINES FOR CHECKING THE LINEARITY OF YOUR SCOPE

Here is a successful way to determine if your scope's amplifiers are affecting your measurements. To make this simple check, first connect a signal generator's leads to the scope's vertical and horizontal inputs. Your next step is to adjust both vertical and horizontal gains until you see a diagonal line across the zero point on the graticule. If the line is straight, you're okay. However, if you see a curve in the line, your amplifiers are not linear, and you are probably going to have errors in your measurements.

HOW TO CHECK PHASE
RELATIONSHIPS WITH A SCOPE

Your scope is particularly good for comparing the phase angle of two signals of the same frequency. Just connect one signal to the vertical and one to the external horizontal input (with the scope set at external input). Figure 9-6 illustrates the effect of varying the phase of the voltage applied to one of the inputs.

Pattern (1) indicates that the two signals are exactly in phase. As you make the phase angle greater, the line will open into a broadening ellipse, as seen at (2). When the difference is 90°, the ellipse becomes a circle as at (4). Now, as the phase difference is increased beyond 90°, the circle begins to collapse toward another straight line, but this time the line indicates 180° out of phase.

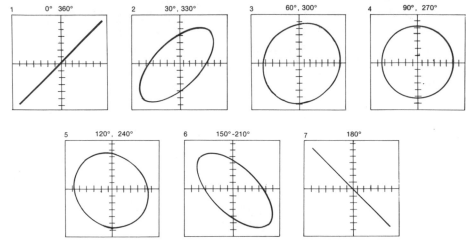

**Figure 9-6: Patterns you will
see on a scope and their
respective relationship**

HOW TO IMPROVE YOUR AC
VOLTAGE MEASUREMENTS WITH
A SCOPE

The advantages of using your oscilloscope as an AC voltmeter are: its high input impedance, its capacity to measure voltages over a very wide frequency range, and its accuracy. You don't have to worry about the type of waveform because the scope will give you a true reading regardless of waveform, if you have it properly calibrated.

The oscilloscope has extremely high input impedance when you place the voltage to be measured directly on the deflection plates. However, it is necessary to know the deflection sensitivity of the CRT. Deflection sensitivity usually is defined as the distance in millimeters that a spot is moved on the screen when one volt is applied to the deflection plates, expressed in millimeters per volt. Most scope graticules are ruled in centimeter graduations. But this is no problem if you just remember that there are 10 millimeters for each centimeter.

Now, the number of millimeters the spot moves—divided by the voltage applied—is the deflection sensitivity. It's easy to see why one volt is used because it works out that whatever distance the spot moves is your CRT deflection sensitivity. In most cases, you'll find the scope sensitivity is 1 mV/cm to 5 V/cm, or 10 mV/cm to 20 V/cm. Incidentally, if you wish to express deflection sensitivity in volts per inch, simply divide 25.4 by your millimeters per volt sensitivity. For example, let's assume that you measure a deflection of 5 millimeters (0.05 centimeters) when you apply one volt to the CRT deflection plates. Next, converting into volts per inch, 25.4/5 = 5.08 volts per inch.

If you use the amplifiers in the scope, the best way to set up your calibration is to place a known voltage of the same waveform as the voltage that you want to measure on the vertical input. As an example, say that you want to measure a sine-wave voltage in peak-to-peak units. The easiest way to do this is to set your vertical gain control so that the applied signal fills a total of 10 vertical lines with a 1 volt signal applied to the vertical input of your scope. The pattern you should see is shown in Figure 9-7.

Let's say you've placed an unknown sine wave voltage on your scope's vertical input, and you have a pattern that fills 20 vertical lines with the attenuation set at 10 to 1. The peak-to-peak value of the voltage under consideration is 200 volts. Should you want to convert the peak-to-peak value to the effective (rms) value, simply multiply whatever your voltage is by 0.3535, which in this case equals 70.7 volts rms.

One final point: You must not touch the vertical gain control once you have the scope calibrated until all voltage measurements you wish to do are completed. If you do move the vertical gain control, you will have to recalibrate the scope before making any further measurements although you can set the scope attenuator to any setting needed without having to recalibrate each new setting.

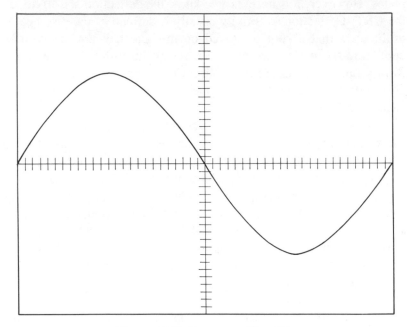

Figure 9-7: Scope calibration

A SIMPLE TECHNIQUE FOR
CHECKING A TV CHASIS WITH
A SCOPE

Many times we all have had a black and white TV chasis without a working picture tube on our workbench. A fast and simple way to check most of the circuits on the chasis is to place the picture on an oscilloscope. The hook-up is quick and easy to make. First, place the scope selector switch in the external sweep position. Next, place a jumper lead from the TV horizontal sweep section to the external sweep input at the oscilloscope. This should produce a horizontal line on the viewing screen of the scope, with all equipment energized.

Now with power off, connect the scope's vertical test probe to the vertical sweep section of the TV receiver. At this point, with power on, you should be able to adjust the vertical and horizontal controls of the scope until you have a square raster on the face of the scope's CRT. You have now established that the low voltage power supply, the horizontal and vertical sweep oscillators and all their components are working properly.

Another step you might like to try is to inject video into the scope. To do this, take a signal off the video amplifier of the TV receiver and place it on the grid or cathode of the scope's CRT to produce beam modulation (sometimes called *Z axis modulation*). In some cases, a beam modulation terminal is placed on the control panel of the oscilloscope. If you can produce a simple picture on the scope, you know that the entire TV set is working properly except that you haven't checked the picture tube and the high voltage section. However, a simple arc check will tell you if you have high voltage or not.

HOW TO CHECK TV
TRANSFORMERS WITH A SCOPE

All technicians who work with TV receivers know that checking horizontal output transformers and yokes can be difficult, to say the least. It's easy to find an open with an ohmmeter. However, finding a short is tricky because the resistance of the coils normally is very low.

In order to check coils with your scope, it's best to make a simple modification. Many technicians immediately "back off" when they hear the word *modification*. But have no fear. In this instance, the modification is really simple. All you need is to take a signal off the cathode or emitter resistor of the scope's horizontal sweep oscillator and bring it out to the front control panel to a jack that you install. The cable you use should be shielded and a capacitor must be in series with the cable and jack as shown in

Figure 9-8. The capacitor can be any value between 500 to 700 picofarads. After you have made the modification, you can check a TV receiver horizontal linearity coil, horizontal output transformer, deflection coil, width coil, or the entire receiver deflection circuit.

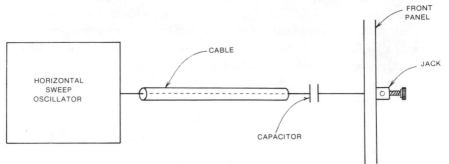

**Figure 9-8: Oscilloscope
modification required for
checking TV transformers**

To check any of the coils—*with the receiver turned off*—connect the scope probe to one end of the coil and then connect the new jack on the scope to the same point. Next, connect the other end of the coil to the ground terminal of the scope. Now vary your scope horizontal sweep rate until you get a pattern on the CRT screen. The pattern you see should look like one of the patterns shown in Figure 9-9 or 9-10.

What you are doing is using the saw-tooth voltage from the scope's horizontal oscillator to produce a ringing waveform on the scope. If the coil is shorted or partially shorted, you'll see the oscillations quickly die out as shown in Figure 9-10. Incidentally, you'll have to use a different sweep setting on your scope with the deflection yoke connected than when it's disconnected. Also, you will have to use lower sweep frequencies with larger inductances than with smaller ones.

To make a simple and quick check of the entire deflection system in a tube-type receiver, merely disconnect the plate cap of the horizontal output tube and connect the pulse and oscilloscope vertical probe to the cap lead of the transformer. Also connect the TV receiver chassis to your oscilloscope ground. If there is a short in the system, you will see the pattern shown in Figure 9-10.

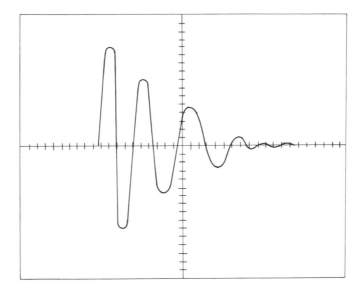

**Figure 9-9: A good coil's
ringing pattern**

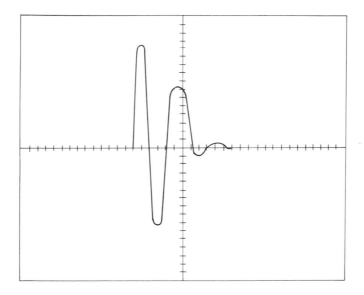

**Figure 9-10: A shorted coil's
ringing pattern**

HOW TO USE YOUR SCOPE TO
CHECK DIODES

You can construct a simple solid state diode tester that may be built into your oscilloscope or constructed as a separate unit. The only parts you will need are a low voltage transformer and one resistor. The wiring diagram is shown in Figure 9-11.

The transformer output is not important except that it is better to use a low voltage type such as a filament transformer. The resistor R_1 should be large enough to restrict current flow to less than 3 mA. For instance, if you use 6.3 volts, the resistor should be 2.7 k ohms. This will produce a current flow of 2.3 mA.

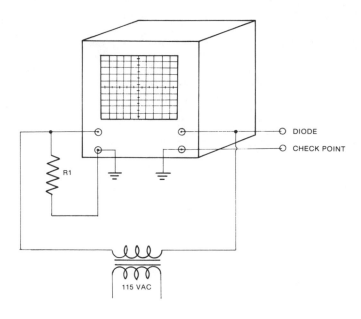

Figure 9-11: Diode tester
schematic

Another good transformer to use is an audio output transformer. In this case, connect the plate side of the transformer to the AC line. As a rule, you'll find that the output voltage is about 2.3

volts. Because you are not placing anything but a very small load on the transformer, the size of the transformer isn't important. However, you do need a current-limiting resistor. For R_1, a 1 k ohm, 1 watt will do in this case. Figure 9-12 shows the typical waveforms you will see and their meanings. Reversing the test leads will cause the L-shaped patterns to reverse position and, finally, you will find a similar type system that you can use to check many other types of components with your scope in Chapter 8.

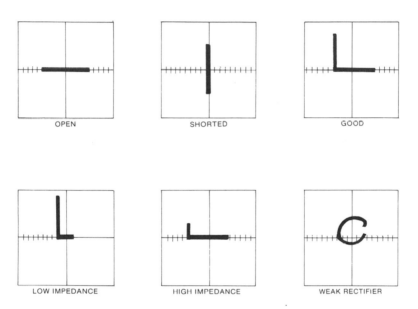

**Figure 9-12: Typical
waveforms seen on a scope
when checking diodes**

Complete Guide to Low-Cost Frequency Measuring Instruments and How to Use Them

10

This chapter contains tips and ideas that can reduce the time spent on frequency measuring jobs from all day to hours, and jobs that may take hours can be cut down to minutes. It also tells you what instrument is best to use, with a step-by-step example of how to make the test in each case.

Technicians who don't know how to design an impedance matching pad are really in deep water when they encounter an impedance mismatch. Actually, while the design formulas may look quite complex in an electronics reference handbook, they can be reduced to two simple calculations, using nothing but two or three resistors. This chapter is full of simple test procedures and construction projects that you can use in your day-to-day work. They will help you get every frequency measuring job out of the shop faster and, in some cases, with superior performance. In other words, you'll find that this chapter doesn't freeze on any single attack. It is very flexible. The whole idea is to help you get the most out of your test instruments, speed up your production, and increase your income.

GUIDE TO USING A FREQUENCY COUNTER

A counter is the most accurate, convenient, and easiest instrument you can get to measure frequency. You can build one (complete plans and construction details were given in the magazine *Radio Electronics*, September 1977) or purchase one in low-cost kit form.

One medium-priced kit is produced by Heathkit and is guaranteed to measure up to 30 MHz with 1 Hz resolution. It also can be used in the period mode to measure intervals up to 9.999 seconds. That's hard to beat when you consider that it comes in an easy to assemble kit. Figure 10-1 shows this versatile counter.

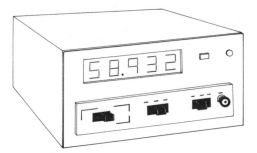

Figure 10-1: Low-cost digital readout frequency counter

A frequency counter is very easy to use, but there are a few words of caution. For example, like most electronic test instruments, it is sensitive to temperature. If you mount one in an automobile with a CB mobile unit—or the like—temperatures can vary from below zero to over 130°F, and many counters will not operate over this range without drifting beyond a usable tolerance.

As another illustration, it's common practice to stack one instrument on top of another on a workbench to save space. However, this isn't always a good practice, especially in the case of a frequency counter because if the instrument it's stacked with is a heat generating device, it can cause your counter to drift out of tolerance.

It's also important to ground your counter in most measurements. *But watch it!* If you're using a three-wire power line power outlet, the shielded lead shouldn't be used with the Heathkit counter if you are going to measure the power line frequency. If you use the shielded lead *it may cause fire to fly* because it's possible to set up a short through the lead, chasis, and grounding wire. A good rule to remember is: Regardless of what type counter (or any other type test instrument, etc.) you are using, when in doubt always check with your voltmeter for a difference of potential between two grounding points *before connecting them*.

Another area that can be troublesome when using a counter concerns the hook-up cables. If you're measuring pulses with an amplitude greater than 200 millivolts and having a rise time shorter than 50 nanoseconds, it is very possible that you'll have dampened oscillations in your connecting cables, and these can cause serious errors in your measurement readings. If this does happen, try placing a 10 k ohm resistor in series with the counter's input cable.

Generally speaking, you can use a direct connection to measure frequency with a counter if the equipment under test has an output power of one-half watt or less. However, if you're measuring the frequency of a transmitter with a higher output power, it's necessary to use a coupling device. For example, a small coil (2 or 3 turns) placed across the ends of the counter test cable works well as a coupling device. To check the frequency, simply place the coil near the transmitter's output terminals. In some cases where the transmitter output is very strong, it may be necessary to excite nothing but the transmitter's master oscillator. Leave all power off the succeeding stages and place the coupling coil near the master oscillator.

While we're talking about measuring the frequency of a transmitter, it's a good time to bring up the fact that it's important to remember that a *transmitter may be damaged by reflected energy* (a high VSWR) *if the transmitter output is not properly terminated.* This is one reason you should always use a dummy load of the proper impedance when making frequency checks if the transmitter isn't connected to its regular antenna.

An excellent example of the use of a frequency counter is to check the frequency of a CB transceiver transmitter because it must remain within the 0.005% tolerance (approximately 1850 Hz) prescribed by the FCC. Again, temperature is important because it isn't uncommon for mobile rigs to be subjected to seasonal temperature extremes, and some CB rigs just can't hold within the authorized tolerance at these extremes. Therefore, when checking the frequency of a CB transceiver, you should check it at the lowest and highest temperatures you expect the rig to operate in.

During your measurements, it's a good practice to vary the transceiver supply voltage while monitoring the frequency. Improper supply voltage (for instance, a low battery voltage) can also cause the frequency to drift beyond the legal—and usable—frequency tolerance.

Some frequency counters are designed to operate while mounted in a vehicle. If you have one of these, it's a good idea to check a mobile CB rig (or any other type mobile transmitter) for mechanical stability during actual mobile operation. The reason you should do this is because a mobile rig is subjected to tremendous vibrations that can cause the frequency to drift out of tolerance.

SERVICING TECHNIQUES USING A FREQUENCY MARKER

Like the sine square-wave generator, the frequency marker doesn't measure anything. But it's a handy low-cost instrument that can be used with a radio receiver to determine just where a certain frequency is, inside the limits of a particular bandwidth, and sometimes that's all you want to know. The marker generator needn't be anything but a stable oscillator generating a series of harmonics based on its fundamental frequency. Typically, a crystal-controlled multivibrator, dual gate IC, or transistor oscillator is used, operating at a fundamental frequency of 100 kHz. Figure 10-2 shows a block diagram of the equipment set-up for measuring a transmitter frequency to determine if it's inside a specific bandwidth.

Many amateur radio operators have short wave radio receivers with a built-in crystal-controlled calibrator for calibrating at 100 kHz intervals. If you have one of these receivers, it isn't necessary to use an external harmonic generator, as shown in Figure 10-2. To check the frequency of a transmitter, turn on the receiver, frequency

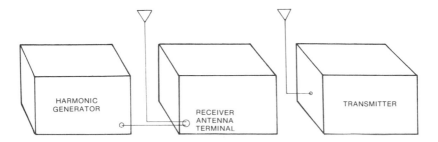

**Figure 10-2: Test set-up for
measuring a transmitter
frequency using a marker
generator and radio receiver**

marker, and transmitter and let them warm up for about one-half
hour or so. Don't key the transmitter during this warm-up period.
The following is a step-by-step method for obtaining a reasonably
accurate frequency check.

Step 1. Key the transmitter and tune the receiver until you are
on the transmitter's carrier and record the receiver dial reading.

Step 2. Tune the receiver to the nearest marker frequency
above and below the transmitter's carrier frequency and record the
two dial readings and frequency of each marker.

Example:

Let's say you are checking a transmitter that is radiating a
signal in the 80 meter radio amateur band. Your notes should look
something like the example shown in Figure 10-3, in this case.

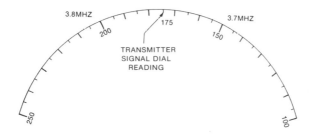

**Figure 10-3: Using a marker
generator to determine a radio
transmitter frequency**

In this instance, and assuming you are using a 100 kHz marker generator, you should find a marker frequency at 3.5, 3.6, 3.7, 3.8, and 4 MHz across the 3.5 to 4 MHz band, provided the marker generator's higher harmonics are strong enough. The next two steps are as follows:

Step 3. Determine the frequency (in hertz) per dial division.

$$\text{Hz / div} = \frac{\text{change in freq}}{\text{change in div}} = \frac{3.8 \text{ MHz} - 3.7 \text{ MHz}}{200 - 150}$$

$$= \frac{100,000}{50} = 2,000 \text{ Hz per division}$$

Step 4. Determine what frequency is indicated at the transmitter dial reading (175). To do this, you need to know how many divisions 175 is above the known point (150). By taking the difference, we get 25 divisions between the two points.

Next, we want to know how much frequency increase there is from the known marker frequency to the unknown transmitter frequency. To find this quantity, simply multiply 25 div × 2,000 Hz per division and we get 50 kHz. Now we know that the frequency at the dial reading 175 is 50 kHz higher than at the dial reading 150, where the known frequency is 3.7 MHz. So to find the frequency of the transmitter, 3.7 MHz + 50 kHz equals 3.75 MHz. This is 250 kHz below the top end of the authorized band and, when you take into consideration that the *safety allowance* usually is taken to be about 3 kHz, it's apparent that we're well within our allowed limits.

USING A LOW-COST SINE-WAVE GENERATOR TO CHECK AMPLIFIER FREQUENCY RESPONSE

Chapter 3 told you that a sweep generator is better than a sine-wave generator for testing an audio amplifier frequency response, which is true. However, if you don't have a sweep generator or the money to buy one, it makes little difference which one is the best or easiest to use. All you're interested in is getting the job done with a minimum of cost with the equipment you have on hand. Sure it's more work to make a point-to-point measurement of the frequency response using a sine-wave generator and the following procedure, but you still can get very good results and not have to come up with the money for a new sweep generator.

A typical sine-square-wave generator is the Heathkit model IG-18, illustrated in Figure 10-4. The sine-wave frequency range is from 1 Hz to 100 kHz. Incidentally, this generator also produces square waves from 5 Hz to 100 kHz, having a rise time of 50 nanoseconds and making it ideal for digital circuit testing.

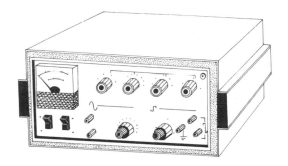

Figure 10-4: Sine-square-wave generator

When measuring the frequency response of an audio amplifier, you'll need a sine-wave generator, VTVM, and sometimes an impedance matching circuit between the signal generator and amplifier, as well as a terminating resistor at the output of the amplifier. Figure 10-5 shows the test set-up using an L-pad attenuator. With this test set-up, you measure the voltage input and the output voltage of the amplifier. Then the ratio of the input voltage to the output voltage is used to compute the amplifier frequency characteristics.

If the amplifier has a fairly flat frequency response, you should make your measurements with the output set to about 8 to 10 dB below its maximum output level, where you'll be pretty safe so far as overdriving the amplifier is concerned. However, if the amplifier doesn't have a fairly flat frequency response, the best way to attack the problem is to check which test frequency will produce the largest output level, and then use this frequency as your reference. If you don't, it's possible you will overload the amplifier and get erroneous readings.

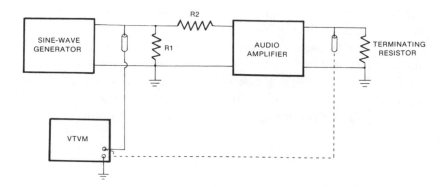

**Figure 10-5: Test set-up for
measuring the frequency
response of an audio amplifier**

If an attenuator is needed between the output of the signal generator and the input of the amplifier, the type will depend on the amplifier's input characteristics. The network you will need may be balanced or unbalanced, and you can use a variable or fixed attenuator; however, it must provide an impedance match between your signal generator and the amplifier under test. In many cases, you can connect a sine-square-wave generator directly to the equipment under test and not worry about impedance matching. Never-the-less, it's a good practice (and sometimes a necessary one) to place a blocking capacitor in series with the test lead to prevent any DC voltage from feeding from the equipment under test into your signal generator. If you do need an impedance matching circuit, refer to Chapter 3 where you'll find Figures 3-12 and 3-13 show the required values needed to construct the most frequently needed matching pads. If you want to design your own, probably the easiest type to build is an L-type. Figure 10-6 shows the wiring diagram.

The side labeled Z_1 is the low impedance input, and the side labeled Z_2 is the high impedance output. To calculate the resistor values, all you need to know is the output impedance of your signal generator (Z_1) and the input impedance of the equipment under test (Z_2) and use the following formulas:

$$R_1 = Z_1 / \sqrt{1 - Z_1 / Z_2} \qquad R_2 = Z_2 \sqrt{1 - Z_1 / Z_2}$$

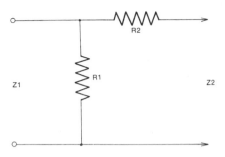

**Figure 10-6: Wiring diagram
for an L-type pad**

If you need a balanced pad, use the same formulas and procedure as was just explained, except you'll have to divide the value of
your calculations for resistor R_2 by 2 to determine the values for the
two resistors marked R_2 in Figure 10-7.

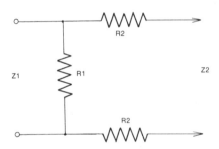

**Figure 10-7: Wiring diagram
for a balanced pad**

STEP-BY-STEP GUIDE
TO MEASURING THE
INPUT IMPEDANCE OF AN
AUDIO AMPLIFIER

To construct the attenuator pad shown in Figure 10-6 or 10-7,
you need to know the input impedance of the audio amplifier under
test. When making the measurement, all you have to do is use the
same basic principle for measuring a meter's internal resistance that

was explained in Chapter 8. Figure 10-8 is an illustration of the test set-up for measuring the input impedance of an audio amplifier.

Using the test set-up shown in Figure 10-8, you may have to make several different settings on the resistor substitution box to obtain a convenient reading on the voltmeter. However, your first step is to short out the resistor substitution box and set your sine-wave generator to about 25 Hz. Don't use a frequency much higher than this because you will start getting reactance effects due to the amplifier input capacitance, which will cause your readings to be in error. Now, adjust the signal generator output level so the voltmeter reading is an even reading that can be reduced to one-half during the next step.

At this point, remove the shorting test lead and then adjust the resistor substitution box until the voltmeter reads one-half your first reading. Finally, read the resistance value from the resistance substitution box. This is the input impedance of the amplifier.

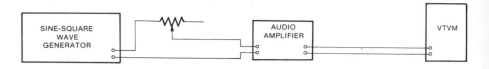

**Figure 10-8: Test set-up for
measuring an audio amplifier
input impedance**

HOW TO USE AN OSCILLOSCOPE
AS A SINE-WAVE DISTORTION
ANALYZER

To check for frequency distortion being produced by an audio amplifier, one of the simplest ways is to display the amplifier output and input on your scope and compare the two. The trick is to know what the scope display is telling you. As we all know, if the input and output signal of the amplifier both appear exactly the same on the scope at all selected test frequencies, the amplifier isn't distorting the sine-wave generator input signal. However, it's possible that you'll see scope presentations that look like one of the examples shown in Figure 10-9, using a sine wave as a test signal.

Here's what the scope patterns are telling you.

1. If you see a pattern on your scope similar to this one, it's an indication of about 10% 2nd harmonic distortion.

2. This is a worse case of 2nd harmonic distortion. In fact, it's an extremely bad case.

3. Here you're getting about 10% 3rd harmonic distortion.

4. This pattern is showing about 20% 3rd harmonic distortion.

5. If you see this pattern, you have a very, very bad case of 3rd harmonic distortion.

6. This scope pattern is showing 4th harmonic distortion.

7. If you see a pattern similar to this one, decrease the output

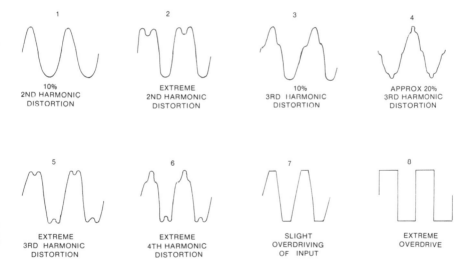

Figure 10-9: Distortion patterns that may be seen on a scope when testing an audio amplifier with a sine wave

level of your signal generator because you are beginning to overdrive the amplifier.

8. Assuming you're using a sine wave input signal to the amplifier, this pattern tells you that you are really overdriving the amplifier. Try decreasing the signal generator output level quite a bit, and you should see a nice clean sine wave if the amplifier isn't producing any other type distortion.

PRACTICAL GUIDE TO USING AN AUDIO OSCILLATOR TO MEASURE THE FREQUENCY RESPONSE OF AN AUDIO FILTER

As always, it's important that you match the impedance between your signal generator and equipment under test. If you're measuring the frequency response of an audio filter and don't know the input impedance, you can measure it using the same procedure used to check an audio amplifier input impedance that was described in this chapter. Once you know the filter's input impedance, you can use the wiring diagram shown in Figure 10-6 and the associated formulas to make a simple L-type pad to match the equipment. The test set-up for measuring the filter frequency response is shown in Figure 10-10.

The output of the filter under test should be terminated in a resistance equal to the filter output impedance. When making the measurement, be sure and connect your VTVM ahead of the attenuator pad, as shown. If you make your reading at the input of the filter, you'll run into two problems. One, you'll probably get erroneous readings due to the reactance produced by the filter's capacitance and inductance. The other problem concerns the signal level after the attenuator pad. It usually will be very low and may not be easy to see on your VTVM.

Another area where you can get into trouble is when the sensitivity of your VTVM isn't sufficient to measure the signal below the cutoff frequency of the filter. If you run into this problem, the solution is to place an amplifier with a *known gain* between the filter

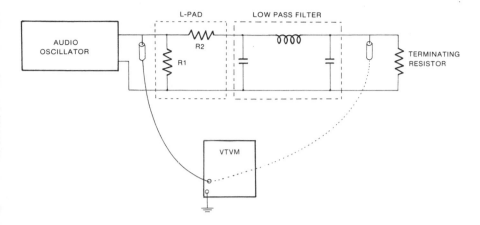

**Figure 10-10: Test set-up for
measuring the frequency
response of an unbalanced
low-pass audio filter**

and your VTVM. The higher the input impedance the amplifier has
(at least 10 k ohms or more), the better. Also, the amplifier should
have a flat frequency response. If in doubt, check it.

A final word of caution. When you are designing an attenuator
pad, it is important that you use a signal level input to the filter that
is recommended by the manufacturer, due to the fact that the characteristics of the iron core used in these filters may change at different
signal levels.

How to Get the Most Out of
Low-Cost TV Test Equipment

11

In this chapter you'll read about how to handle TV test instruments with greater skill, which leads to faster, more profitable TV servicing. You'll find every page full of useful know-how on TV test equipment, with complete instrudtions on how to avoid troubles when using this type gear.

As an illustration, many times technicians become totally confused when it becomes necessary to figure signal strength with and without a matching transformer placed between an antenna, field strength meter, and TV receiver. You'll find out not only what's happening in this case—you'll also find a simple one-step solution to the problem.

You'll find many other simplified practical ways to deal with all types of TV tests and a large variety of time-saving techniques that will improve your ability to use a low-cost scope, color bar generator, alignment generator and field strength meter.

USING A LOW-COST SCOPE FOR
TV SIGNAL TRACING

A low-cost oscilloscope is ideal for TV signal tracing purposes, provided you understand that some of them have certain limitations. For instance, probably you'll have no trouble from the second video detector right on through the video amplifiers to the picture tube grid or in the sound section. But, place your demodulator probe on the input of the second IF amplifier (assuming there are three IF amplifier stages in the receiver), and chances are you won't see anything on your scope. You'll also find the same situation at the input to the first IF, mixer and RF amplifier. However, as was just explained, don't let this keep you from signal tracing with a low-cost scope. For example, if you use a *demodulator probe* and touch the output of the last IF stage and find a signal there, your next step is to use a high-impedance probe and check the output of the second detector. If you see the same waveform at both check points, the second detector is good. If not, you've located the bad circuit.

After the detector—and assuming you had a signal out of it—the video signal leaves the detector and passes through the video amplifier and into the video output. A typical video scope display is shown in Figure 11-1. The pattern is what you should see on the output of the first video amplifier.

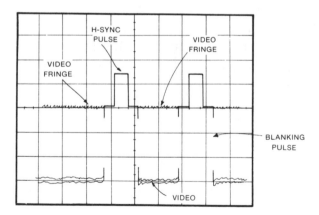

**Figure 11-1: Oscilloscope
display of a horizontal sweep
rate video signal**

When you're using a *scope* and *high impedance test probe*, your best bet during initial signal tracing, is to check the inputs and outputs of the video stages. Most of the time you'll find the factory service notes have pictures of the correct waveforms. As an illustration, Figure 11-2 shows what the horizontal sweep rate to a picture tube grid should look like if the set is working properly. Notice the polarity is reversed in respect to the output of the first video amplifier. You will find this happens between each stage as you check the video section.

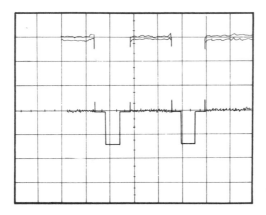

**Figure 11-2: Scope display of
the signal input to a picture
tube grid**

What you want to do is compare the peak-to-peak voltage pictures given in the factory notes to the waveform on your scope and see if the shape of the video signal and relative peak-to-peak voltages are similar to those the manufacturer prescribes. Any deviation from the manufacturer's information indicates trouble in the receiver circuit in that area.

USING AN OSCILLOSCOPE TO
CHECK THE SYNC SECTION

A low-cost scope will do a fine job of tracing vertical and horizontal sync signals through the sync circuits. You'll get the best results with a *high impedance probe* when you are signal tracing in these circuits. There are several different ways to process the sync signals, but frequently you'll find they are taken off the video detector or video amplifier and passed on to a sync separator. After they leave the sync separator, the signals will go to the vertical and horizontal oscillators.

When you check the vertical sync at the output of the separator, you should see a signal similar to the one shown in Figure 11-3A. All you'll probably see are slight dips or small pips as shown, which are the vertical sync pulses. Touch the scope test probe to the various components in the vertical sync section, starting at the sync take-off line, and where you find the peak-to-peak value is incorrect or the appearance has abnormal pattern deviations, this is where the trouble area lies. Use the same procedure to check the horizontal sync section except you should see a scope presentation like the one shown in Figure 11-3B.

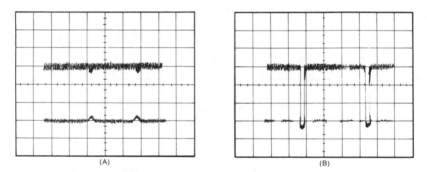

**Figure 11-3: Scope display at
output of sync separator**

PRACTICAL TECHNIQUES FOR
CHECKING COLOR TV RECEIVERS
WITH A LOW-COST SCOPE

You can trace signals in color TV receivers but, like the black and white sets, you may have to restrict your testing to the last IF, luminance (also called the *Y signal*) section, color demodulator, and following components. Also, you can monitor the output signal of the 3.58 MHz oscillator to see if it's operating. Although it's possible you won't see anything but a solid CW signal with a low-cost scope, you'll be fairly safe, assuming the oscillator is working properly, if you see the horizontal sweep pattern on the scope increase in amplitude when you test it. You must remember, however, that the pattern can vary in apparent amplitude by a change of the scope controls.

You can also use a low-cost scope to check the color section of a color TV receiver. It's better to connect a color bar generator to the receiver antenna terminals when testing this section. Start off by looking at the outputs of the R-Y and B-Y demodulators.

In most integrated circuit receivers, luminance information is added either in the demodulator chip itself or directly into the chroma output amplifiers. You can get a good clean scope presentation of the R-Y and B-Y signals by shunting the luminance signal to ground with a capacitor of about 80 pF. What you should see on the scope is shown in Figure 11-4.

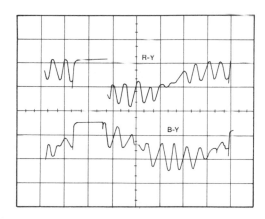

**Figure 11-4: R-Y and B-Y
output signals**

If the chroma outputs aren't correct, backtrack to the bandpass amplifier output, and you should see a pattern similar to the one shown in Figure 11-5. Your next step is to measure the inputs to the

R-Y and B-Y amplifiers. You should see about the same pattern at the input to the amplifiers as you do at the demodulators. Another test point is the G-Y amplifier. Its output should look about the same as the R-Y and B-Y amplifiers.

One check that is often overlooked (or not understood) is the placement of the color bars in reference to zero. If you will look at your scope very closely, you'll see they don't pass through zero at the same point. For example, you should see the R-Y signal passing through zero at the sixth bar, the B-Y signal passing through zero at the third and ninth bars, and the G-Y passing through zero at the seventh bar. When you're servicing the color circuits, its extremely important these three signals pass through zero exactly as explained. If they don't, its an indication the color signals are not properly processed. As a general rule, it's a good idea to make this test anytime you replace resistors or capacitors in the color section. In some instances, you'll find it's necessary to closely match and use the same value component as the original.

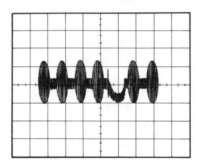

**Figure 11-5: Bandpass
amplifier output signal**

KEY STEPS TO USING A COLOR
BAR GENERATOR

A color alignment generator is one of the best test instruments around for color TV servicing. For example, the Heathkit model IG-5240 color alignment generator is about the size of a small hand-held calculator and will produce the sixteen displays shown in Figure 11-6, on the picture tube of a TV receiver. These displays can be used for complete color TV alignment and convergence adjustments.

When using a color alignment generator, you'll find the rainbow pattern (also called *color bars*) is the most important for troubleshooting the color section of a color TV, and the dot patterns are

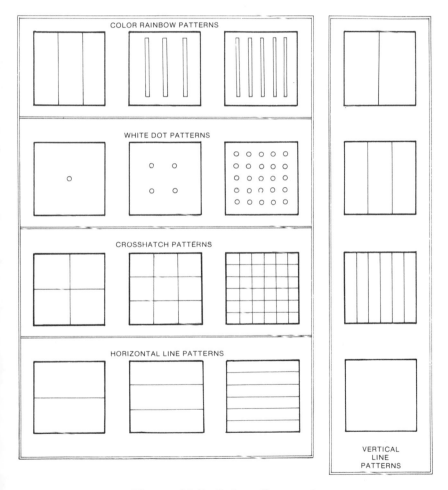

**Figure 11-6: Color alignment
generator patterns**

best for performing the first part of the convergence adjustments. The crosshatch patterns are used for linearity and the second part of the convergence adjustments. Linearity adjustments are made on the receiver until both the horizontal and vertical lines are equally spaced. Figure 11-7 is an illustration of poor vertical and horizontal sweep linearity.

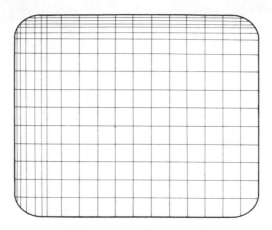

Figure 11-7: Crosshatch pattern showing incorrect linearity

A standard color bar pattern produced by many color bar generators consists of ten color bars across the TV receiver picture tube. Once you understand the screen presentation, these are a great help when you're troubleshooting a color TV receiver. Figure 11-8 shows the ten bars, their colors and phase relation.

Here are some of the things you can do with these color bars. You can check the phase relation between the color signals, adjust for correct signal amplitudes in the matrix circuit, and inject the signal into the RF, IF, demodulator, and video amplifier stages. As another example, if you see one of the three primary colors missing, it's telling you that your first step should be to check the corresponding color difference amplifier (if there is one).

Referring to Figure 11-8, you can see the color bar generator causes the TV receiver screen to display a color bar every 30° of

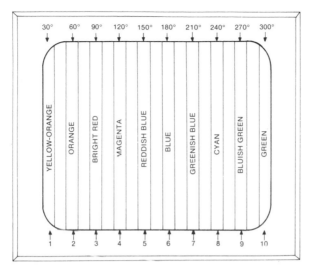

Figure 11-8: Color bar patterns

phase shift in reference to the color burst (0° reference point), assuming the receiver has no malfunctions. The horizontal blanking pulse occupies the time between 330° to 360°. Therefore, there is no presentation during this period. Table 11-1 lists the color bars and their associated signals.

The color bar generator produces the rainbow pattern by generating two signals that are out of phase by the correct number of degrees for each color. If the color pattern is not keyed, the display will be a continuous color pattern (one color blending into another). Therefore, these portions of the display not wanted are blanked out. The result is the color bars you see.

When you're using a color bar generator, you may run into a case where all colors are there but not in the proper proportions. In this case, it's probably one of the two demodulators (in some sets, these are the X and Z demodulators) that is not working properly. If you see a strong blue but weak red and green, check the X demodulator. A bad Z demodulator will produce a grayish-orange presentation, having weak blue and green in the picture.

As you can see by referring to Figure 11-6, a color alignment generator can give you white dots, horizontal lines, vertical lines, crosshatch patterns and a single dot and line. As was mentioned

BAR #	COLOR	SIGNAL
1	YELLOW-ORANGE	——
2	ORANGE	+I
3	RED	+(R-Y)
4	MAGENTA	-(G-Y)
5	REDDISH BLUE	+Q
6	BLUE	+(B-Y)
7	GREENISH BLUE	——
8	CYAN	-I
9	BLUISH GREEN	-(R-Y)
10	GREEN	+(G-Y)

**Table 11-1: Color bar colors
and their associated color
signals**

before, the dots are used for dynamic convergence adjustments. The crosshatch pattern can be used, but the dots are ideal to start with.

To make the adjustments, the color dot bar generator is attached to the TV receiver antenna terminals with the receiver set at one of the low VHF channels (Heathkit model IG-5240 generator is calibrated for channel 4). Dots are sent into the TV, and the entire TV screen will display the dots. The idea is to merge the three dots—red, green and blue—together until they produce a single white dot. This part of the adjustment is called the *static adjustment*, and only the center of the screen is adjusted.

The crosshatch patterns are better to use to correct the top, bottom, left and right side of the screen. If the color set is out of adjustment, you'll see red, green and blue crosshatch patterns on the screen. You want to merge them until you see a white crosshatch pattern, as nearly perfect as possible.

You will find twelve adjustments on the back of this type color TV that are used during convergence. Many color receivers today do not have these twelve adjustments because they are not needed in a precision in-line picture tube (nor in a single gun picture tube set). Just about everything is preset at the factory.

USING A MARKER/SWEEP GENERATOR FOR TV ALIGNMENT

Quite a bit was said about sweep generators in Chapter 3, and how to use a dip meter as a marker generator was explained in Chapter 7. However, this section contains many more tips for using a marker/sweep generator and how it is used to align TV receivers. If you use a marker/sweep generator and scope correctly, it will enable you to see exactly what the bandpass characteristics of the IF stages of a TV receiver are. There is no more guesswork and, therefore, you'll turn out superior work which, of course, means happy customers and more profit. Furthermore, a sweep generator can be used for FM aligning and as a signal source for troubleshooting.

Figure 11-9 shows the six frequencies that are important to you when you are aligning a TV receiver. The sweep generator should be operating at a center frequency of 44.25 MHz and its sweep set so it sweeps from below an IF amplifier's circuit resonance to above it, to produce this pattern on your scope. The scope leads may be connected to the detector load resistor. However, if the sweep generator is connected to the antenna terminals of the receiver, the frequency used for alignment purposes is frequently 67.25 MHz (channel 4).

It's very important for you to realize that you must have the manufacturer's service and alignment notes to align a TV receiver according to factory specifications unless you're very familiar with the set. These notes and a schematic of the receiver usually can be

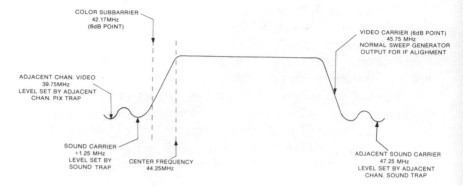

**Figure 11-9: Sweep generator
frequencies and scope display
of video detector output**

purchased at an electronic supply house in any fairly large city.

You'll probably find you will need various special "hook-ups" and bias voltages for different AGC and IF strip designs on the service notes. Modern marker/sweep generators such as the Heathkit model IG-57A have built-in adjustable bias supplies—in fact, this one has two—so normally you shouldn't have any trouble with the required bias voltages.

Now, back to the use of the sweep generator and scope. Sweep generators usually come with an external sweep output that *should* be connected to the sweep input of your scope. When you do this, you'll probably see a pattern on the scope something like the one shown in Figure 11-10.

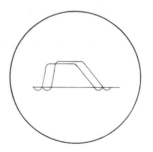

**Figure 11-10: Scope pattern
indicating an out-of-phase
condition**

To eliminate the two images, simply adjust the *phase control* on the sweep generator until you see a single trace on your scope. The reason most sweep generators have a phase control and external sweep output terminal is to permit you to use the sweeper with any oscilloscope regardless of what type sweep your scope uses— sawtooth or sine wave.

The marker generator (or separate marker, as explained in Chapter 7) is of primary importance in today's TV servicing. Although dip meters and absorption wave meters can be used, a sweep generator with a built-in crystal-controlled marker generator is, by far, the easiest and best type to use.

RULES FOR SUCCESSFUL USE OF A SWEEP GENERATOR

Rule 1. Your first step should be to set all traps at their proper frequency. These are given in Figure 11-8 in this chapter.

Rule 2. Next, check for overloading. An easy way to do this is to place a VTVM across the detector output and vary your sweep generator output signal level. When the VTVM voltage reading remains constant, it's an indication you are overdriving the set. To correct the problem, reduce the sweep generator output until you see the VTVM's reading vary as you change the sweep generator output level. This is an extremely important check and should be done at the beginning of each trap and IF adjustment, *especially if you are working with a stagger-tuned IF strip*.

Rule 3. Don't connect the output of a sweep generator (typically 75 ohms) directly to the antenna terminals of a TV receiver (300 ohms). You'll find construction details for an inexpensive impedance matching pad in Chapter 7, Figure 7-8.

Rule 4. Do use a DC blocking capacitor in series with the sweep generator test lead when aligning the different stages. It also may help to place an RF bypass capacitor on your scope input lead.

Rule 5. Don't try tracking on a TV receiver front end with a low-cost sweep generator and scope even though the manufacturer's notes include instructions and recommend you do it. In fact, it's very probable you won't see any signal on your scope if you try the mixer section, as was explained earlier in this chapter.

Rule 6. Make darned sure your marker generator is accurate. See Chapter 7 for a general discussion of how you can check this.

Rule 7. Follow the manufacturer's service notes for bias. Frequently, you'll have to ground the AGC bias line to prevent the AGC from affecting the output readings.

Finally, the sweep generator is excellent for aligning stagger-tuned IF stages. The frequencies for trap and IF alignment are shown in Figure 11-11. As you can see, when you align a stagger-tuned color TV receiver, it's necessary to change the frequency of your sweep generator several times. For this reason, it's easy to overload the circuits. See *Rule 2* for an easy way to prevent this from happening.

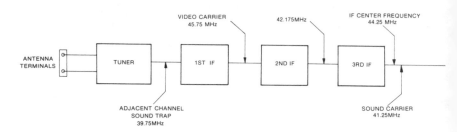

**Figure 11-11: Stagger-tuned
TV alignment frequencies**

HOW TO USE A FIELD-STRENGTH
METER AND GET PROFESSIONAL
RESULTS

When you're working in a weak signal area, nothing can save you as much time and work when you are installing an antenna as a field-strength meter. Also, a field-strength meter is excellent for making an accurate measurement of the output signal level of an RF signal generator, plus it can be a handy tool for TV troubleshooting.

As an illustration, suppose you have a weak picture on a TV receiver. Obviously this can be antenna problems, poor reception area, trouble in the tuner, or loss of gain in the IF stages. In a case like this, your first step is simply to measure the signal strength at the receiver end of the antenna lead-in. This will let you know whether the trouble is in the receiver or antenna system. If you get a signal strength reading between 1,000 and 4,000 microvolts (0 dB to + 12 dBmV), you can be sure the trouble is in the receiver. However, it should be pointed out that in fringe areas you may have to work with *field-strength* readings as low as 500 microvolts, and most ordinary field-strength meters won't budge off the pin with readings at this level.

Now, let's suppose you are in a weak signal area and are trying to place a TV antenna in the best reception position. One way to do this is to have the customer watch the TV receiver and call you when the best picture is observed. A much better way is to attach a field-strength meter (typically, it is light weight and battery operated) to the antenna and place the antenna at various heights and locations while you're looking for the strongest signal spot.

Usually, field-strength meters have a 75 ohm input impedance, and most TV antennas have a 300 ohm output impedance. Therefore, it's important to remember to use an all-channel-matching transformer that converts 300 ohms to 75 ohms when you are making tests like these.

UNDERSTANDING SIGNAL
STRENGTH READINGS

Much confusion is found when you talk to different technicians about signal strength. Actually, the readings you get from a field-strength meter don't mean a whole lot except as a comparison. And this comparison is valid only when the readings are taken with the same antenna each time a measurement is made.

Let's say you're using a field-strength meter with extra high sensitivity, and you measure 500 microvolts at the output of a 300 ohm antenna. Then the signal is fed through an all-channel-matching transformer into a 75 ohm coax cable that has zero line loss, and at the output of the coax you measure a signal strength of 250 microvolts. Does this mean you have only one-half of your signal left? Not really. Remember the rule that states: "Power out must equal power in, in a perfect system"? This rule says that although the voltages have changed, we still have the same signal power. A few calculations will prove the point.

First, using the formula $P = E^2/R$ at the antenna, we find the power is 833.3 picowatts. Next, using the 250 microvolt reading at the 75 ohm cable output, we again get a value of 833.3 picowatts, which means there really isn't a loss of signal power. It's important you keep this in mind when you're working with different impedances and signal strengths with a directly connected field-strength meter or any other type measuring instrument.

PRACTICAL GUIDE TO DETERMINING THE OUTPUT SIGNAL OF AN IMPEDANCE MATCHING TRANSFORMER

When you are trying to get good TV reception where the signal strength is very poor, every microvolt counts. A field-strength meter will serve you well in these tough situations. However, the reading you get on the field-strength meter after it passes through the impedance matching transformer will not be the actual voltage that will be fed to the receiver, as explained in the preceding section.

To determine what the receiver will receive when it's connected to the antenna (assuming the receiver, lead-in, and antenna are all the same impedance), it's necessary to use some multipliers. Multiply the field-strength meter readings by the following numbers to find out the number of microvolts that will be at the receiver antenna terminals. For TV channels 2 through 6, multiply the field-strength meter reading by 1.1, TV channels 7 through 13 use 1.4 and TV channels 14 through 83 use 3.0. These values will work well, assuming you're using a 75 ohm field-strength meter that is matched to a 300 ohm TV antenna lead-in with an all-channel-matching transformer.

Servicing with Vectorscopes, Tube Checkers and CRT Tester/Rejuvenators

12

A vectorscope is a valuable color television receiver test instrument that can be used to perform all chroma signal adjustments and help make color TV servicing easier, faster and more accurate.

Another piece of test gear that can be very useful—and sometimes essential if you don't have a substitute tube—for radio/TV servicing is a tube checker. In the following chapter you'll not only learn all about these instruments, you'll also find effective ways to make rapid TV receiver measurements as well as successful CRT rejuvenation techniques.

PRACTICAL GUIDE TO UNDERSTANDING A VECTORSCOPE

With the introduction of both low-cost vectorscopes and solid state color TV receivers, TV waveform analysis has become a science rather than an art. In hybrid and tube sets we could get away with marginal operation, but solid state receivers can go completely wild if a single transistor or **IC** isn't doing its job. With manufacturers announcing no more tube receivers, the days of tube substitutions are coming to an end. Therefore, we all must take the analytical approach in our servicing, and a low-cost vectorscope can be the ticket to success for this type work. However, before you can become an expert using a vectorscope, you've got to understand the beast.

Most of us know that if two sine-wave signals of the same frequency are applied to the vertical and horizontal inputs of an oscilloscope, a phase relationship (or Lissajous) pattern will appear on the screen. If the two signals are 90⁰ out of phase, you'll see a circle, but if the difference is about 135⁰ or so, you'll see an oval similar to the one shown in Figure 12-1.

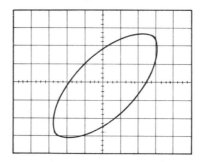

**Figure 12-1: Lissajous pattern
showing a phase difference
between two sine waves**

This same set-up also can produce a pattern that looks like a daisy if you connect the scope probes to the red and blue chroma outputs (R-Y and B-Y signals) of a color TV receiver with a color bar generator connected to its antenna terminals. Figure 12-2 shows the basic connections for producing a vectorscope display on an ordinary oscilloscope.

Can you use an ordinary oscilloscope and color bar generator to service a color TV receiver? You sure can. However, all we're

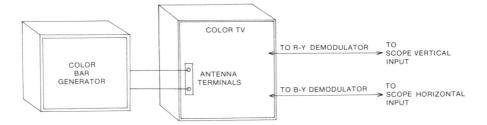

**Figure 12-2: How a vectorscope
display can be achieved with
an oscilloscope, using two
high impedance probes and a
color bar generator**

trying to point out here is that a vectorscope is nothing more than an oscilloscope with a special faceplate related to a vector diagram. We'll discuss how to service with the set-up presently. In the mean-time, what you'll see with the hook-up shown in Figure 12-2 is shown in Figure 12-3.

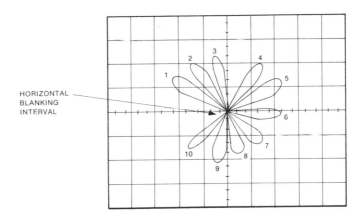

**Figure 12-3: A vectorscope
display on a scope using R-Y
and B-Y signals from a color
TV receiver**

You can see there are ten petals on the daisy pattern shown in Figure 12-3. Each of the petals corresponds to one of the ten standard color bars, and it is 30° from the start of one petal to the start of the next, in an idealized pattern. Figure 12-4 shows the R-Y and B-Y outputs and the resulting vectorscope display. Incidentally, if you obtain these two signals from the cathode circuits of the picture tube of the same set, you'll see the same pattern, but it will be reversed in appearance.

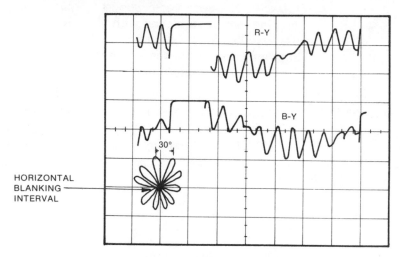

Figure 12-4: Scope display of the R-Y and B-Y output and resulting daisy pattern

NTSC VECTORSCOPE

Some commercial vectorscopes have a special CRT graticule that is used with the daisy pattern to provide accurate phase and amplitude readings. Some have numbered segments to correspond to the 10 standard color bars shown in Chapter 11, Figure 11-6; others have displays showing phase angles and proper amplitudes for adjusting burst phase (the reference signal) and the other color information in TV stations, etc. The burst vector lies on the 180°

gratical line and is adjusted using I and Q test signals out of a bar generator. This type vectorscope viewing screen may be used to adjust the phase and amplitudes required by the Federal Communications Commission as specified by the National Television System Committee (NTSC) and, in general, is quite expensive. It is shown in Figure 12-5.

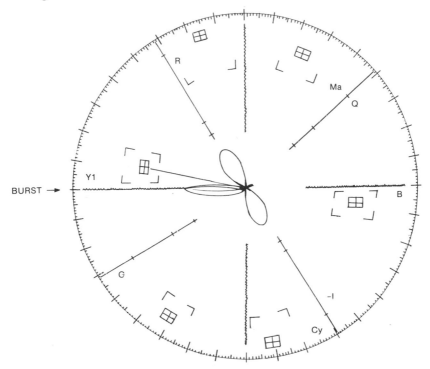

**Figure 12-5: Tektronix
vectorscope (type 520 NTSC)
viewing screen**

LOW-COST VECTORSCOPE

Some vectorscopes produce all the signals needed for purity adjustment, have a rainbow generator built in, and are much, much less expensive. A good example is Heathkit model IO-101. It has color bars, dots, crosshatch, and vertical and horizontal lines. A visual display of all ten color bars in the form of a daisy is shown for color circuit troubleshooting. Figure 12-6 is an illustration of this type scope presentation.

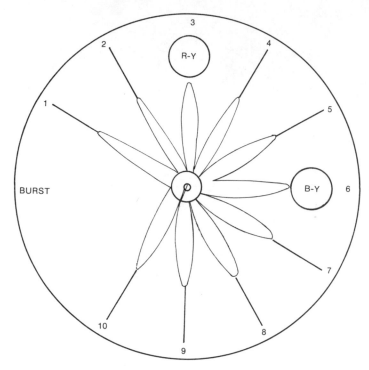

**Figure 12-6: Heathkit
vectorscope/color generator
viewing screen**

The controls for all vectorscopes are the same for the CRT, in other words, horizontal position, vertical position, and intensity. The only difference is that you'll find controls for different channels (2 through 6 on the Heathkit vectorscope), various other test patterns, plus and minus going video signals, etc., that aren't available when you use an ordinary scope. However, using a scope does provide some valuable service information, as we shall see.

HOW TO ANALYZE A VECTORGRAM

With a commercial vectorscope, you'll immediately have the desired daisy display, and chroma troubles can be located rapidly. Therefore, your servicing time is cut to a minimum. The vectorgram can tell you whether or not the bandpass amplifier is tuned properly, if there is enough color amplification, and if there is overloading. It will also show phase relationship. For example, the height of the petals is an indication of the color signal amplitude. Too small means not enough gain or, if you see the petal tops flatten out, it means there is circuit overloading. Should the scope presentation show some petals longer than others, it's an indication of non-linear distortion. Also, the roundness of the petals indicates the bandpass characteristics. The petals should all be there: not too small, not too fat, and not too thin.

Fat petals that tend to overlap mean you possibly have an alignment problem in the IF strip or trouble in the chroma section. Another telltale sign is a blurry petal pattern. In this case, try adjusting the 3.58 MHz trap.

The positioning of the petals provides an indication of correct frequency and phase. For example, referring to Figure 12-6, if the petals are stationary but the third (R-Y) is not pointing straight up to the number three as shown, the phase is off. The same holds true for the sixth (B-Y) petal. If the petals are rotating, there is a color sync trouble. In either case, you may need to adjust the 3.58 MHz color oscillator output circuit because it's probably off frequency or out of phase, and an incorrect signal is being sent to the chroma demodulator.

It's very easy to tell when you have a loss of R-Y input to the vectorscope because you'll have no petals—only a straight horizontal line across the viewing screen. Similarly, you'll get nothing but a vertical line if you don't have a B-Y signal.

WORKING IN THE COLOR
SYNC SECTION

Color sync section alignment normally is very simple with a vectorscope. However, it is a vital procedure in color TV servicing and, if you don't understand what's going on, it can become a maze of confusion. The color bars produced by a color bar generator are locked into place by the color sync section of a color TV receiver (it also locks the colors of a color picture in place).

The 3.58 MHz crystal-controlled oscillator is the heart of the color sync section. If this subcarrier reference is missing or is off frequency, it's possible you will either see the color go wild (if the oscillator is badly mistuned) or no color at all. The oscillator re-inserts the 3.58 MHz subcarrier that was suppressed at the TV station, but the receiver oscillator must run in exactly the same phase and frequency as the incoming burst signal from the station. The way the receiver oscillator is locked in (synchronized) to the TV station timing oscillator is by a reference subcarrier *burst* transmitted on the back porch (interval following horizontal sync pulse) of the composite video signal (Figure 12-7).

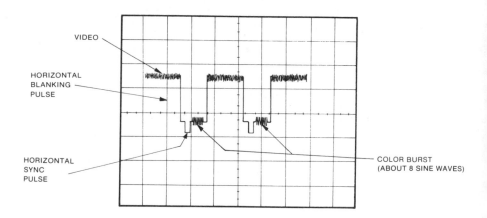

**Figure 12-7: Scope picture
of composite TV signal with
color burst signal**

In the receiver, the burst signal is extracted from the composite video signal, amplified in the burst amplifier and then fed to the 3.58 MHz oscillator for the purpose of synchronizing it to the TV station's color subcarrier generator. Normally, you'll find two outputs from the receiver's subcarrier regenerator circuits—the red reference and blue reference signals that are sent on to the chroma demodulators. Generally speaking, this is the same for tube, transistor, or IC circuit color TV receivers.

When the oscillator is off frequency, an incorrect signal is sent to the chroma demodulator. The result is improper colors on the screen, or the colors will drift (or run) across the screen. If you encounter this type of problem, your best bet is to get out the vectorscope and align the color sync section. For example, if you have a color TV receiver with a reactance control (a lot of receivers don't use this type adjustment), short out the test point between the phase detector and reactance amplifier. Now, you should see the petals on the vectorscope start to turn. Next, adjust the plate coil of the reactance amplifier until the petals turn very slowly. Then remove the shorting jumper wire—the petals should snap into place. If they don't, you have trouble in the reactance circuit. If they take off in a fast rotation, your problem, more than likely, is in the phase detector.

HOW TO TROUBLESHOOT USING A LOW-COST OSCILLOSCOPE AS A VECTORSCOPE

It was stated at the beginning of this Chapter that you could use any low-cost scope as a vectorscope. However, there are limitations when doing this. For instance, you won't get a pattern with as accurate a vectorgram from this type set-up as you will from a commercial vectorscope. But, this doesn't mean you can't do a pretty good job with nothing but your scope, high impedance probes and color bar generator. With an ordinary scope, you're just going to have to work a little harder.

What you will see on the scope screen will look more or less like a daisy, but it may be distorted quite a bit although, if you'll *carefully* adjust the scope horizontal and vertical sweep amplitudes, you can get a pretty fair daisy. Also, it will help quite a bit if you'll make a special faceplate for your scope, showing the idealized placement of the color bars and their angles, as shown in Figure 12-8.

How do you analyze the vectorgram? Exactly the same way as was explained in the previous pages. The length of the petals, the roundness of the petals, and the position of the petals indicate signal amplitude, bandpass response, and phase of the chroma signals.

One of the best ways to learn to analyze a vectorgram is to set up a color bar generator and scope on a color receiver known to be in good working order and look at the pattern this produces, so you'll know what to try for during chroma adjustments.

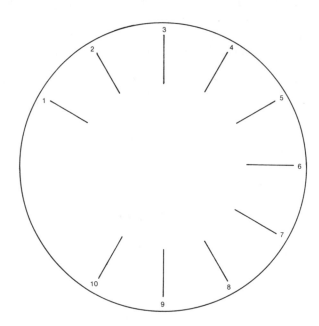

**Figure 12-8: How to construct
a special faceplate to convert
a low-cost scope to a
vectorscope**

SOME IMPORTANT POINTS ABOUT
TUBE CHECKERS AND TESTERS

There is little doubt that the best test for a tube is a direct substitution of a known-good tube. Many TV service shops don't even own a tube tester and, most of the time, wouldn't use it if they had one. But, notice I said *most of the time*. In other words, there are times when they come in handy. For instance, it's simply impossible to stock every tube that can be encountered in day-to-day servicing. If a tube is suspected as defective and you don't have a known-to-be-good replacement, the tube tester is about the only way to check it out. Also a dynamic mutual conductance (or transconductance) tube tester can provide valuable information concerning a tube's condition and probable lifespan, during routine preventive maintenance checks.

The most common low-cost tube tester is the emission type. This type simply connects all the tube elements, control grid, screen grid, suppressor grid, and plate (if the tube is a pentode) to form a diode and then checks electron emission from the cathode (assuming an indirectly heated cathode tube). The read-out meter usually is calibrated to read BAD - ? - GOOD. Figure 12-9 shows a tube checker meter face used with this instrument.

Another instrument that is *somewhat* better is the dynamic mutual conductance tube tester. This tester has circuits that produce voltages and currents something like the tube experiences under normal operating conditions. Usually a low voltage 60 Hz signal is applied to the control grid, with the other tube elements operating at the tube manufacturer's recommended levels. The mutual conductance is measured and indicated directly on the meter scale— normally calibrated to read in micromhos.

You'll find several switches that are used to select the various tube elements and the tube tester's internal circuits needed for the tube under test. Also, there are dials to let you select the proper bias, plate and heater voltage, with push buttons for making the test. Generally a roll-type tube chart is built right into the instrument and indicates the switch setting and voltages to be set in before you press

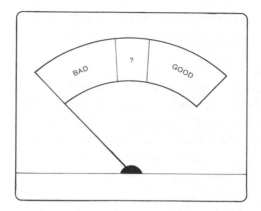

**Figure 12-9: Meter face
generally used on an emission
type tube checker**

the buttons to make the test. These roll charts have to be up-dated from time to time and some companies supply them for their tube checkers on a twice a year basis, for a few dollars. However, it isn't all that uncommon to run into a tube that isn't on the chart. Here's how to whip this problem.

First, you'll need a tube manual or manufacturer's specs that lists the tube voltages for the tube you're working with. One very good and readily accessible source for this information is found in the back of the Radio Amateur's Handbook or in tube manuals sold by radio supply houses. Let's take a 6CL6 tube for example. You'll find its base diagram looks like the one shown in Figure 12-10. You can see that with the base diagram, we know what tube element is connected to each of the nine pins.

Now, it must be remembered that all vacuum tubes are designed to be operated within maximum and minimum ratings. What we're most interested in is the suggested *maximum safe* operating voltages and currents for the tube electrodes because, if we exceed these, there is a possibility of tube damage. Table 12-1 lists these values for a 6CL6 (a power pentode) that can be found in most any tube manual.

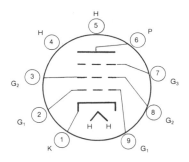

**Figure 12-10: Base diagram
for a 6CL6 receiving tube**

The best procedure while you are learning is to start with a known-good tube that is listed on the roll chart. Set up the voltages on the tube tester (without inserting the tube into the tube socket) using the dials and levers, and then measure each of the points shown in the base diagram. Remember, you count the tube socket top view counter clockwise. In other words, you'll find pin hole 1 at 11 o'clock, pin hole 2 at 10 o'clock, hole 3 at 9 o'clock, and so on. Doing this with one or more known tubes will familiarize you with the function of each of the tube checker levers, etc., and the various voltages they produce at different settings.

Next, using the base diagram of a tube not on the roll chart, set up the voltages on the tube tester (again without the tube in the tube tester socket), using the appropriate dials and levers and measure

HEATER VOLTS	PLATE SUPPLY VOLTAGE	GRID BIAS	SCREEN VOLTAGE	SCREEN mA	PLATE mA	TRANSCON-DUCTANCE	WATTS OUTPUT
6.3V	250V	-3V	150V	7/7.2	31	11K	2.8

**Table 12-1: Recommended
maximum voltages and
currents for a 6CL6 power
amplifier pentode**

each of the connection points shown in the base diagram, to be sure you don't exceed the recommended maximum voltages. Finally, insert the tube and make the test.

It isn't too hard to make your own tube charts for testing unknown tubes. All it takes is a little bit of experimenting and practice. Learning to do this can be particularly handy when working with obsolete tubes. If you really get into a pinch, you don't even need a tube tester. Simply make your connections to the proper tube socket and estimate the voltages by referring to known tubes of about the same size.

Generally speaking, don't exceed 300 volts on the plate, about 20 mA plate current, and use no more than 6 volts (to start) for the filaments when checking miniature receiver tubes. The transconductance should check out somewhere between 4,000 to 8,000 k on these tubes if you're using a tube tester that reads transconductance.

SERVICING WITH CRT TESTER/REJUVENATORS

How to get by with nothing but the simplest tube checker as a CRT rejuvenator was explained in Chapter 4. However, using that system is far too slow and inconvenient in a busy TV service shop. The reason is that there are several different hook-ups needed from set to set. For example, the tube sockets needed are: 14 pin for 90° color tubes, 13 pin for in-line color tubes, and 7 pin or 8 pin for black and white tubes. Figure 12-11 is an illustration of a simplified pushbutton type CRT tester/rejuvenator showing the controls and their function. Some of the CRT problems that can be corrected with this instrument are: low CRT cathode emission, heater-to-cathode leakage and opens and shorts.

Many tester/rejuvenators (such as the one shown) can give an indication of the life remaining in the CRT and have individual grid current meters for each color gun. In this tester, the red gun meter is used to check black and white picture tubes.

To quickly check a picture tube (or any other type CRT) to see if there is a good possibility it may be rejuvenated, darken the room

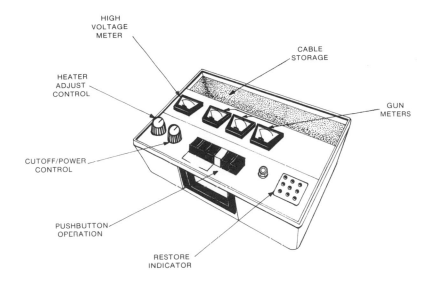

HIGH
VOLTAGE
METER

CABLE
STORAGE

HEATER
ADJUST
CONTROL

GUN
METERS

CUTOFF/POWER
CONTROL

PUSHBUTTON
OPERATION

RESTORE
INDICATOR

**Figure 12-11: CRT
tester/rejuvenator**

and see if you can see even the smallest glimmer of light on the CRT with the brightness control full on. If you can see any light at all, there's a good chance you can rejuvenate the tube. Of course, this is assuming the set has good high voltage and all other circuits are working properly and there are no shorts.

After you've made this quick check, your next step is to connect the tester to the CRT and check the cathode emission. If your reading is low, or even if you read no emission, try to rejuvenate the tube. But remember, when you try to rejuvenate a CRT, it's possible you'll completely burn out the heaters, and this should be explained to a customer. Explain that all you are trying to do is save him the cost of a new picture tube and that his tube must be replaced if the rejuvenation doesn't work. Furthermore, there is no guarantee how long the tube will last: maybe one minute or maybe a year or more.

Index

203